DAVID VENNOR-MORRIS

christs.

VECTOR ANALYSIS

The New University Mathematics Series

Editor:
Professor E. T. DAVIES
Department of Mathematics, University of Southampton

This series is intended for readers whose main interest is in mathematics, or who need the methods of mathematics in the study of science and technology. Some of the books will provide a sound treatment of topics essential in any mathematical training, while other, more advanced, volumes will be suitable as preliminary reading for research in the field covered. New titles will be added from time to time.

BROWN and PAGE: *Elements of Functional Analysis*
BURGESS: *Analytical Topology*
COOPER: *Functions of a Real Variable*
CURLE and DAVIES: *Modern Fluid Mechanics* (Vols. 1 and 2)
PORTEOUS: *Topological Geometry*
RUND: *The Hamilton-Jacobi Theory in the Calculus of Variations*
SAMET: *Numerical Analysis*
SMITH: *Laplace Transform Theory*
SMITH: *Introduction to the Theory of Partial Differential Equations*
SPAIN: *Vector Analysis*
ZAMANSKY: *Linear Algebra and Analysis*

Vector Analysis

BARRY SPAIN

Head of the Department of Mathematics
Sir John Cass College, London

D. VAN NOSTRAND COMPANY LTD
LONDON
TORONTO   NEW YORK
PRINCETON, NEW JERSEY

D. VAN NOSTRAND COMPANY LTD.
Windsor House, 46 Victoria St., London, S.W.1

D. VAN NOSTRAND COMPANY INC.
120 Alexander Street, Princeton, New Jersey
24 West 40 Street, New York 18

D. VAN NOSTRAND COMPANY (CANADA) LTD.
25 Hollinger Road, Toronto 16

Library of Congress Catalog Card No. 65–13629

Made and printed in Great Britain by
William Clowes and Sons, Limited
London and Beccles

Preface

The treatment in this book emphasizes at all times that a vector is an entity in itself and should not be considered merely as a triple of numbers. Consequently, proofs by means of Cartesian coordinates are avoided.

The first chapter contains the basic elements of vector algebra, which are applied in the following chapter to the geometry of the straight line and the plane. The third chapter discusses the fundamentals of vector calculus, and applications to differential geometry are made in the fourth chapter. The contents of this chapter, with the exception of the Frenet formulae, curvature and torsion, are required for later developments of the theory.

Line integrals, surface integrals and volume integrals play an important role in vector analysis. Many students will meet these concepts before they have had formal courses in them. Consequently the fifth chapter presents a concise account of these topics.

The following three chapters are respectively devoted to the gradient, divergence and curl of a vector. Of these, the first is defined in terms of the directional derivative whilst the latter two are defined by limits of integrals. In this way the theory is developed independently of any coordinate system. The operator ∇ is not introduced, as the author has observed that this is a dangerous tool in the hands of the inexperienced.

There follow chapters on Stokes's theorem, Green's theorems and orthogonal curvilinear coordinate systems.

The concluding chapter provides a link between vector and tensor analysis. It includes a discussion on the physical components of a vector as distinct from the components referred to a general basis. There is some confusion in the literature of vectors about the validity of the equation curl curl $\mathbf{a} = $ grad div $\mathbf{a} - \Delta\mathbf{a}$ referred to a curvilinear

v

coordinate system. Some authors in fact define $\Delta\mathbf{a}$ by means of this equation. However, at this point a so-called *natural* basis is introduced with respect to which this equation can be deduced.

No attempt has been made to apply vectors to problems in mathematical physics. Indeed, a comprehensive treatment which would do justice to those applications would necessitate a threefold expansion of this book.

A representative selection of examples is inserted at appropriate places and answers are provided at the end of the book.

During the preparation of this book, I have been greatly indebted to Dr. J. H. Wilkinson who read the manuscript and made many valuable suggestions which have been incorporated in the work.

My thanks are also due to my colleagues Dr. M. G. Smith and Mrs. R. J. Church, the former for a critical reading of the manuscript and the latter for the supply of a number of examples. For help in reading the proofs I wish to thank my wife and elder son.

Finally, I wish to express my appreciation to the staff of the publishers for their cooperation and for their help with the diagrams.

B. S.

Contents

CHAPTER 1

Vectors

1 Vectors

Physical quantities such as mass, temperature and work are measured by numbers referred to some chosen unit. These numbers are called **scalars.**

Other quantities exist such as displacement, velocity, acceleration and force, which require for their complete specification a direction as well as a scalar. These quantities are called **vectors** and may be represented by a straight line with an arrow.

Fig. 1

Formally, a **vector** is a *directed line segment.* The vector depicted in Fig. 1 from the point P, called the **initial point**, to the point Q will be denoted by $\overrightarrow{PQ}$. It has the **length** or **magnitude** PQ and the direction from P to Q as indicated by the arrow.

In the special case when Q coincides with P, we refer to the *zero vector* $\overrightarrow{PP}$ denoted by **0**. This vector has zero magnitude but indeterminate direction.

In addition to the notation $\overrightarrow{PQ}$ for a vector, it will be convenient to designate a vector by a letter in bold type such as **A, a, α,** etc.

The magnitude of a vector **a** will be denoted by either $|\mathbf{a}|$ or a and it is well to emphasize that the magnitude of a non-zero vector is a positive quantity.

A vector of unit magnitude is called a **unit vector**. The letters **i, j, k** and **I, J, K** are reserved for unit vectors.

Two vectors are said to be *equal* if they have the same magnitude

1

and direction. Geometrically, all vectors obtained from the vector $\overrightarrow{PQ}$ by a translation in space are equal.

EXERCISE

1. Which of the following are scalars and which are vectors? (*a*) volume, (*b*) energy, (*c*) momentum, (*d*) temperature, (*e*) work, (*f*) electric field intensity.

2 Addition of Vectors

The addition of two vectors is defined by the so-called triangle or parallelogram law.

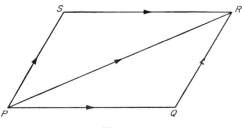

Fig. 2

Let $PQRS$ in Fig. 2 be a parallelogram. Formally we define the sum of the vectors $\overrightarrow{PQ}$ and $\overrightarrow{QR}$ to be the vector $\overrightarrow{PR}$ represented by the third side of the triangle PQR.

Since the vectors $\overrightarrow{QR}$ and $\overrightarrow{PS}$ are equal, we may also define the sum of the vectors $\overrightarrow{PQ}$ and $\overrightarrow{PS}$, which have the same initial point P, to be the vector $\overrightarrow{PR}$ represented by the diagonal through P of the parallelogram formed by PQ and PS.

Let us write

$$\overrightarrow{PQ} = \overrightarrow{SR} = \mathbf{a}, \qquad \overrightarrow{PS} = \overrightarrow{QR} = \mathbf{b}.$$

By the triangle law of addition, both the sum of $\overrightarrow{PQ}$ and $\overrightarrow{QR}$ and the sum of $\overrightarrow{PS}$ and $\overrightarrow{SR}$ are equal to $\overrightarrow{PR}$. It follows that

$$\mathbf{a}+\mathbf{b} = \mathbf{b}+\mathbf{a}.$$

That is, vectors satisfy the *commutative* law of addition.

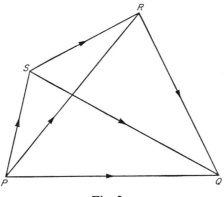

Fig. 3

With reference to Fig. 3 let us write

$$\overrightarrow{PS} = \mathbf{a}, \quad \overrightarrow{SR} = \mathbf{b}, \quad \overrightarrow{RQ} = \mathbf{c}.$$

By the triangle law of addition we have

$$\overrightarrow{PR} = \mathbf{a+b}, \quad \overrightarrow{SQ} = \mathbf{b+c}.$$

Further applications of the triangle law yield

$$(\mathbf{a+b})+\mathbf{c} = \overrightarrow{PR}+\overrightarrow{RQ} = \overrightarrow{PQ} = \overrightarrow{PS}+\overrightarrow{SQ} = \mathbf{a+(b+c)}.$$

That is, vectors satisfy the *associative* law of addition and so there is no ambiguity if either expression is written without brackets in the form $\mathbf{a+b+c}$.

Figures 4 (*a*), (*b*) and (*c*) show that in the case when $\overrightarrow{PQ}$ and $\overrightarrow{QR}$ are parallel, the triangle law yields the result

$$\overrightarrow{PQ}+\overrightarrow{QR} = \overrightarrow{PR}$$

whether the arrows along $\overrightarrow{PQ}$ and $\overrightarrow{QR}$ are in the same or opposite directions. To avoid confusion the arrows are not drawn in the figures.

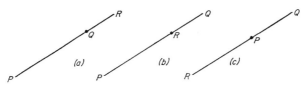

Fig. 4

At this stage it is well to point out that a physical quantity may be specified by a direction and magnitude and yet not be a vector because it does not obey the vector law of addition. Finite rotation of a rigid body is such a quantity.

3 Subtraction of Vectors

If the vector **a** is represented by the directed displacement $\overrightarrow{PQ}$, we define $-\mathbf{a}$ to be the vector represented by $\overrightarrow{QP}$. Hence

$$\mathbf{a} - \mathbf{a} = \mathbf{0}.$$

Now we may define the difference $\mathbf{a} - \mathbf{b}$ of two vectors **a** and **b** to be the sum of the vectors **a** and $-\mathbf{b}$. That is,

$$\mathbf{a} - \mathbf{b} = \mathbf{a} + (-\mathbf{b}).$$

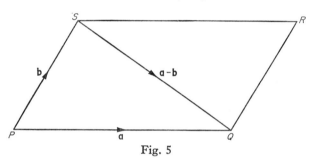

Fig. 5

Let $\overrightarrow{PQ}$ and $\overrightarrow{PS}$ in Fig. 5 represent the vectors **a** and **b** respectively. Complete the parallelogram $PQRS$. It follows from the triangle law of addition and the definitions of the negative of a vector and subtraction that

$$\begin{aligned}
\mathbf{a} - \mathbf{b} &= \overrightarrow{PQ} - \overrightarrow{PS} \\
&= \overrightarrow{PQ} + \overrightarrow{SP} \\
&= \overrightarrow{SP} + \overrightarrow{PQ} \\
&= \overrightarrow{SQ}.
\end{aligned}$$

That is, the difference of two vectors can be represented by a diagonal of a parallelogram.

EXERCISES

1. Show that $|\mathbf{a} + \mathbf{b}| \leqslant |\mathbf{a}| + |\mathbf{b}|$.
2. Show that $|\mathbf{a} - \mathbf{b}| \geqslant ||\mathbf{a}| - |\mathbf{b}||$.

3. Under what conditions do we obtain equality signs in the inequalities of Exercises 1 and 2?

4 Multiplication of a Vector by a Scalar

If λ is a scalar and $\mathbf{a}$ is a vector, $\lambda\mathbf{a}$ is defined to be the vector with the same direction as $\mathbf{a}$ if λ is positive, the opposite direction to $\mathbf{a}$ if λ is negative, and with magnitude $|\lambda|$ times the magnitude of $\mathbf{a}$. Consequently we have

$$|\lambda\mathbf{a}| = |\lambda|\,|\mathbf{a}|.$$

Note carefully that $|\mathbf{a}|$ denotes the magnitude of the vector $\mathbf{a}$ whilst $|\lambda|$ denotes $+\lambda$ or $-\lambda$ according as λ is positive or negative. Also we see that $\mathbf{a}/a$ is the unit vector in the direction of $\mathbf{a}$.

It follows immediately that

$$\lambda(\mu\mathbf{a}) = \mu(\lambda\mathbf{a}) = \lambda\mu\mathbf{a}$$

and

$$(\lambda+\mu)\mathbf{a} = \lambda\mathbf{a}+\mu\mathbf{a}.$$

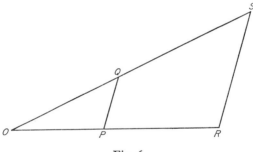

Fig. 6

Let OPQ (Fig. 6) be the triangle whose sides $\overrightarrow{OP}$, $\overrightarrow{PQ}$ and $\overrightarrow{OQ}$ represent the vectors $\mathbf{a}$, $\mathbf{b}$ and $\mathbf{a}+\mathbf{b}$ respectively. Let RS, parallel to PQ, cut OP and OQ in R and S. Then we have

$$\frac{OR}{OP} = \frac{RS}{PQ} = \frac{OS}{OQ}.$$

Denoting these equal ratios by λ, it follows that $\overrightarrow{OR}$, $\overrightarrow{RS}$ and $\overrightarrow{OS}$ represent the vectors $\lambda\mathbf{a}$, $\lambda\mathbf{b}$ and $\lambda(\mathbf{a}+\mathbf{b})$ respectively. Hence by the triangle law of addition we have

$$\lambda(\mathbf{a}+\mathbf{b}) = \lambda\mathbf{a}+\lambda\mathbf{b}$$

and so we are permitted to remove brackets in the usual algebraical manner.

Two vectors **a** and **b** are **co-directional** if $\mathbf{a} = \lambda\mathbf{b}$, where λ is positive; that is, if **a** and **b** are parallel and have the same direction.

EXERCISES

1. If **a** and **b** are vectors whose directions are neither parallel nor coincident, show that the relation $\lambda\mathbf{a} + \mu\mathbf{b} = 0$ implies that both λ and μ are zero.

2. If P is any point and D, E, F are the mid-points of the sides BC, CA and AB respectively of the triangle ABC, show that

$$\overrightarrow{PA} + \overrightarrow{PB} + \overrightarrow{PC} = \overrightarrow{PD} + \overrightarrow{PE} + \overrightarrow{PF}.$$

5   Point of Division

Let R in Fig. 7 divide the join of A and B in the ratio $AR/RB = \lambda$. Then $\overrightarrow{AR} = \lambda\overrightarrow{RB}$.

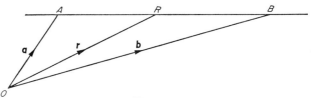

Fig. 7

Further, let A, B and R be given by the vectors **a**, **b** and **r** referred to the fixed initial point O. Then we have

$$\mathbf{r} - \mathbf{a} = \lambda(\mathbf{b} - \mathbf{r}),$$

from which it follows that

$$\mathbf{r} = \frac{\mathbf{a} + \lambda\mathbf{b}}{1 + \lambda}.$$

In particular, we see that the mid-point of AB is given by the vector $\frac{1}{2}(\mathbf{a} + \mathbf{b})$.

When the three points A, B and R are collinear, the previous result shows that a number λ exists such that

$$\mathbf{a} + \lambda\mathbf{b} - (1 + \lambda)\mathbf{r} = 0.$$

Hence three non-zero numbers α, β and γ exist such that

$$\alpha\mathbf{a} + \beta\mathbf{b} + \gamma\mathbf{r} = 0$$

and

$$\alpha + \beta + \gamma = 0.$$

Conversely, given that $\alpha\mathbf{a}+\beta\mathbf{b}+\gamma\mathbf{r}=\mathbf{0}$, where α, β and γ are three non-zero numbers satisfying $\alpha+\beta+\gamma=0$, there is no loss in generality if we assume that $\alpha+\beta\neq0$. Hence we have

$$\mathbf{r} = \frac{\alpha\mathbf{a}+\beta\mathbf{b}}{\alpha+\beta}$$

and so R lies on AB and divides it in the ratio β/α.

The vectors $\mathbf{a}$, $\mathbf{b}$, $\mathbf{c}$, ..., $\mathbf{l}$ are said to be **linearly dependent** if we can find a set of scalars λ, μ, ν, ..., ρ, not all zero, such that

$$\lambda\mathbf{a}+\mu\mathbf{b}+\nu\mathbf{c}+\cdots+\rho\mathbf{l} = \mathbf{0}.$$

Otherwise they are **linearly independent.**

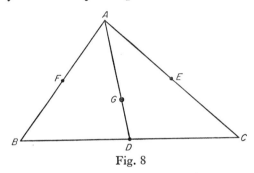

Fig. 8

Example 1. Prove that the medians of a triangle meet at a point which divides each median in the ratio $2:1$.

Let A, B and C be given by the vectors $\mathbf{a}$, $\mathbf{b}$ and $\mathbf{c}$. Then the mid-points D, E and F (Fig. 8) are given by $\frac{1}{2}(\mathbf{b}+\mathbf{c})$, $\frac{1}{2}(\mathbf{c}+\mathbf{a})$ and $\frac{1}{2}(\mathbf{a}+\mathbf{b})$. Let G be the point which divides AD in the ratio $2:1$. Then G is given by the vector $\frac{1}{3}(\mathbf{a}+\mathbf{b}+\mathbf{c})$. Similarly G lies on BE and CF and so the result is established.

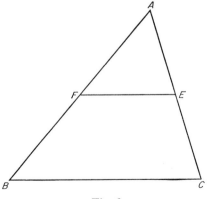

Fig. 9

Example 2. Prove that the line joining the mid-points of two sides of a triangle is parallel to the third side and is equal in length to half that of the third side.

In Fig. 9 let A, B and C be given by the vectors $\mathbf{a}$, $\mathbf{b}$ and $\mathbf{c}$. Hence the mid-points E and F are given by $\frac{1}{2}(\mathbf{c}+\mathbf{a})$ and $\frac{1}{2}(\mathbf{a}+\mathbf{b})$. Accordingly $\overrightarrow{FE} = \frac{1}{2}(\mathbf{c}+\mathbf{a}) - \frac{1}{2}(\mathbf{a}+\mathbf{b}) = \frac{1}{2}(\mathbf{c}-\mathbf{b})$. But $\overrightarrow{BC} = \mathbf{c} - \mathbf{b}$ and so the result is established.

EXERCISES

1. Show that the mid-points of the sides of a skew quadrilateral form the vertices of a parallelogram.

2. Show that four points A, B, C, D, no three of which are collinear, given respectively by the vectors $\mathbf{a}$, $\mathbf{b}$, $\mathbf{c}$ and $\mathbf{d}$ are coplanar if and only if four non-zero numbers α, β, γ and δ exist such that

$$\alpha\mathbf{a}+\beta\mathbf{b}+\gamma\mathbf{c}+\delta\mathbf{d} = \mathbf{0} \quad \text{and} \quad \alpha+\beta+\gamma+\delta = 0.$$

3. Show that the lines joining the mid-points of the opposite edges of a tetrahedron are concurrent and bisect each other at the point of concurrency.

4. The **centroid** G of the points A_1, A_2, ..., A_n with associated numbers m_1, m_2, ..., m_n is defined by the equation

$$\overrightarrow{OG} \sum_{r=1}^{n} m_r = \sum_{r=1}^{n} (m_r \, \overrightarrow{OA_r}).$$

Show that the position of G is independent of the choice of the initial point O.

6   Components of a Vector

Let $\overrightarrow{OP}$ (Fig. 10) represent the vector $\mathbf{a}$ and $\overrightarrow{OU}$ the *unit* vector $\mathbf{u}$ which makes an angle α with $\mathbf{a}$. Let the perpendicular from P to OU intersect it at L. The length OL, multiplied by plus or minus one

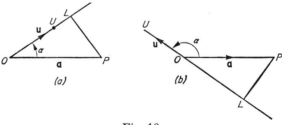

(a)   (b)

Fig. 10

according as OL is in the same or the opposite direction to OU, is called the **component** of $\mathbf{a}$ in the direction $\mathbf{u}$. In either case the component is $a \cos \alpha$. Further, the vector $a \cos \alpha$ **u** is called the **projected vector** of **a** in the direction **u**.

The projected vector of **a** on a plane is defined to be the projected vector of **a** in the direction of the line of intersection of the given plane and the plane through **a** perpendicular to the given plane.

Consider (Fig. 11) the vectors $\overrightarrow{OP}=$**a** and $\overrightarrow{PQ}=$**b** and the unit vector $\overrightarrow{OU}=$**u**. Let PL and QM be perpendicular to the direction OU. The components of the vectors **a** and **b** in the direction **u** are OL and LM respectively. The sum of **a** and **b** is represented by the vector $\overrightarrow{OQ}$ which has the component OM in the direction **u**.

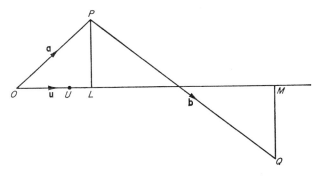

Fig. 11

Accordingly the sum of the components of two vectors in a given direction is equal to the component of the sum of the two vectors in that direction.

This result clearly extends to any number of vectors. That is, the sum of the components of any number of vectors in a given direction is equal to the component of their sum in that direction.

EXERCISES

1. $ABCDEF$ is a regular hexagon whose sides are of length 5 units. If $\overrightarrow{AB}=$**a** and $\overrightarrow{BC}=$**b**, find the following vectors in terms of **a** and **b**: (i) $\overrightarrow{CD}$, (ii) $\overrightarrow{DE}$, (iii) $\overrightarrow{EF}$, (iv) $\overrightarrow{FA}$, (v) $\overrightarrow{DA}$, (vi) $\overrightarrow{EB}$. Further, obtain the components of $\overrightarrow{FA}$ and $\overrightarrow{FE}$ along $\overrightarrow{BD}$ and $\overrightarrow{AB}$ respectively.

2. $ABCD$ is a regular tetrahedron whose edges are of length 3 units. If $\overrightarrow{AB}=$**α**, $\overrightarrow{BC}=$**β** and $\overrightarrow{CD}=$**γ**, find the vectors $\overrightarrow{AD}$ and $\overrightarrow{CA}$ in terms of **α**, **β** and **γ**. Further, calculate the projected vector of $\overrightarrow{AD}$ along $\overrightarrow{CA}$.

7 Fundamental System of Vectors

Introduce (Fig. 12) a *right-handed* system of mutually orthogonal coordinate axes OX, OY and OZ. That is, a right-handed corkscrew rotating through a right-angle from OY to OZ advances in the positive direction OX. Similarly, if the corkscrew rotates through a right-angle from OZ to OX or OX to OY it advances in the directions of OY and OZ respectively. A *left-handed* system is obtained if the direction of any one of the axes is reversed. We shall always select the axes to form a right-handed system.

The three unit vectors **i**, **j** and **k** in the positive directions of the coordinate axes are called a **fundamental system** of vectors.

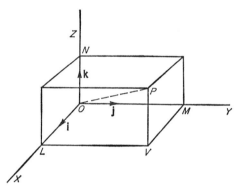

Fig. 12

Let **a** represent the vector $\overrightarrow{OP}$. Complete the rectangular parallelepiped with diagonal OP and edges through O along the axes. It is clear from the figure that OL, OM and ON are the components of **a** in the directions of **i**, **j** and **k** respectively and that the projected vectors are $\overrightarrow{OL}$, $\overrightarrow{OM}$ and $\overrightarrow{ON}$.

By the repeated application of the triangle law of addition of vectors we have

$$\mathbf{a} = \overrightarrow{OP} = \overrightarrow{OV} + \overrightarrow{VP} = \overrightarrow{OL} + \overrightarrow{LV} + \overrightarrow{VP}$$
$$= \overrightarrow{OL} + \overrightarrow{OM} + \overrightarrow{ON}$$

and so

$$\mathbf{a} = a_i\mathbf{i} + a_j\mathbf{j} + a_k\mathbf{k},$$

where a_i, a_j and a_k denote respectively the components of **a** relative to the fundamental system.

Further, we have

$$OP^2 = OV^2 + VP^2 = OL^2 + OM^2 + ON^2,$$

and so

$$a^2 = a_i^2 + a_j^2 + a_k^2.$$

EXERCISES

1. If $\mathbf{a} = 4\mathbf{i} + \mathbf{j} - \mathbf{k}$, $\mathbf{b} = 3\mathbf{i} - 2\mathbf{j} + 2\mathbf{k}$ and $\mathbf{c} = -\mathbf{i} - 2\mathbf{j} + \mathbf{k}$, calculate (i) $\mathbf{a} + \mathbf{b} + \mathbf{c}$, (ii) $|\mathbf{a} - \mathbf{b} - \mathbf{c}|$, (iii) a unit vector parallel to $2\mathbf{a} - \mathbf{b} - \mathbf{c}$ but in the opposite direction.

2. Prove that the vectors $\mathbf{i} - \mathbf{k}$, $-\mathbf{i} + \mathbf{j} + 2\mathbf{k}$ and $\mathbf{i} - \mathbf{j} - 3\mathbf{k}$ can form the sides of a triangle.

8   Scalar Product

The **scalar product** of two vectors $\mathbf{a}$ and $\mathbf{b}$ is defined to be the scalar $ab \cos \theta$, where θ is the angle between the vectors $\mathbf{a}$ and $\mathbf{b}$. The scalar product corresponding to the vectors $\mathbf{a}$ and $\mathbf{b}$ in Fig.

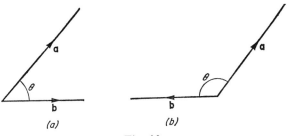

(a)   (b)

Fig. 13

13(a) is positive since θ is acute, while the scalar product in Fig. 13(b) is negative since θ lies between $\pi/2$ and π.

We agree to denote the scalar product by $\mathbf{a} . \mathbf{b}$ and so it is sometimes referred to as the 'dot' product. (Other notations may be met, such as $\mathbf{a}|\mathbf{b}$, $(\mathbf{a}, \mathbf{b})$.) We have

$$\mathbf{a} . \mathbf{b} = ab \cos \theta.$$

It follows that

$$\mathbf{a} . \mathbf{b} = \mathbf{b} . \mathbf{a}.$$

That is, scalar products satisfy the *commutative* law of multiplication.

From the definition, $\mathbf{a} . \mathbf{b} = 0$ if either $a = 0$, $b = 0$ or $\cos \theta = 0$. In the latter case the vectors $\mathbf{a}$ and $\mathbf{b}$ are mutually orthogonal. Conversely, the scalar product of two orthogonal vectors is always zero.

Again, we have from the definition that the scalar product $\mathbf{a}.\mathbf{b}$ of two co-directional vectors $\mathbf{a}$ and $\mathbf{b}$ is ab. Hence $\mathbf{a}.\mathbf{a}=a^2$. At times it is convenient to write $\mathbf{a}.\mathbf{a}=\mathbf{a}^2$.

The fundamental system of vectors $\mathbf{i}$, $\mathbf{j}$ and $\mathbf{k}$ satisfies the relations

$$\left.\begin{array}{l} \mathbf{i}.\mathbf{i} = \mathbf{j}.\mathbf{j} = \mathbf{k}.\mathbf{k} = 1, \\ \mathbf{j}.\mathbf{k} = \mathbf{k}.\mathbf{i} = \mathbf{i}.\mathbf{j} = 0. \end{array}\right\} \tag{8.1}$$

If λ is a scalar, we see from the definition that

$$\lambda(\mathbf{a}.\mathbf{b}) = (\lambda\mathbf{a}).\mathbf{b} = \mathbf{a}.(\lambda\mathbf{b})$$

and so we can write these equivalent expressions in the form $\lambda\mathbf{a}.\mathbf{b}$.

Another consequence of the definition of the scalar product is that the component of the vector $\mathbf{a}$ in the direction of the unit vector $\mathbf{u}$ is $\mathbf{a}.\mathbf{u}$.

In Section 6 we proved that the sum of the components of two vectors in a given direction is equal to the component of the sum of the two vectors in that direction. It follows (Fig. 11) that

$$\mathbf{a}.\mathbf{u}+\mathbf{b}.\mathbf{u} = (\mathbf{a}+\mathbf{b}).\mathbf{u}.$$

On multiplication by the scalar λ, we have

$$\mathbf{a}.\mathbf{c}+\mathbf{b}.\mathbf{c} = (\mathbf{a}+\mathbf{b}).\mathbf{c}$$

where $\mathbf{c}=\lambda\mathbf{u}$. That is, we may remove brackets in scalar products as in ordinary algebraic multiplication. In other words, scalar multiplication is *distributive* with respect to addition.

Let the vectors $\mathbf{a}$ and $\mathbf{b}$ have components a_i, a_j, a_k and b_i, b_j, b_k respectively with respect to a fundamental system of vectors $\mathbf{i}$, $\mathbf{j}$ and $\mathbf{k}$. Then

$$\mathbf{a}.\mathbf{b} = (a_i\mathbf{i}+a_j\mathbf{j}+a_k\mathbf{k}).(b_i\mathbf{i}+b_j\mathbf{j}+b_k\mathbf{k}).$$

Removal of brackets and use of the scalar product properties (8.1) of the vectors of the fundamental system yield

$$\mathbf{a}.\mathbf{b} = a_ib_i+a_jb_j+a_kb_k.$$

Example 1. Show that the three altitudes of a triangle are concurrent.

Let A, B and C be given by the vectors $\mathbf{a}$, $\mathbf{b}$ and $\mathbf{c}$ referred to some initial point. Further, let (Fig. 14) the perpendicular BY from B to CA intersect the perpendicular AX from A to BC at the point H given by the vector $\mathbf{h}$.

The conditions of orthogonality are

$$(\mathbf{b}-\mathbf{c}).(\mathbf{h}-\mathbf{a}) = 0 \quad \text{and} \quad (\mathbf{c}-\mathbf{a}).(\mathbf{h}-\mathbf{b}) = 0.$$

From the identity

$$(\mathbf{b}-\mathbf{c}).(\mathbf{h}-\mathbf{a})+(\mathbf{c}-\mathbf{a}).(\mathbf{h}-\mathbf{b})+(\mathbf{a}-\mathbf{b}).(\mathbf{h}-\mathbf{c}) = 0$$

we have

$$(\mathbf{a}-\mathbf{b}).(\mathbf{h}-\mathbf{c}) = 0.$$

That is, CH is perpendicular to AB as required.

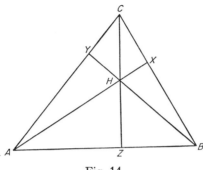

Fig. 14

Example 2. Obtain the acute angle between two diagonals of a cube.

Let the rectangular parallelepiped in Fig. 12 be a cube with edge of length unity and let the perpendicular from P to the XY plane cut it at V. Then the vector $\overrightarrow{OP}=\mathbf{i}+\mathbf{j}+\mathbf{k}$ whilst the vector $\overrightarrow{NV}=\mathbf{i}+\mathbf{j}-\mathbf{k}$. Hence the angle α between the two diagonals is given by

$$|\mathbf{i}+\mathbf{j}+\mathbf{k}|\,|\mathbf{i}+\mathbf{j}-\mathbf{k}|\cos\alpha = (\mathbf{i}+\mathbf{j}+\mathbf{k}).(\mathbf{i}+\mathbf{j}-\mathbf{k}),$$

from which $\cos\alpha=1/3$ and so $\alpha=70°\,32'$.

EXERCISES

1. If $\mathbf{a}.\mathbf{b}=\mathbf{a}.\mathbf{c}$, show that either $\mathbf{a}=\mathbf{0}$, $\mathbf{b}=\mathbf{c}$ or $\mathbf{a}$ is orthogonal to $\mathbf{b}-\mathbf{c}$.

2. Given $\mathbf{a}=\mathbf{i}+2\mathbf{j}-3\mathbf{k}$ and $\mathbf{b}=3\mathbf{i}-\mathbf{j}+2\mathbf{k}$, (i) show that the vectors $\mathbf{a}+\mathbf{b}$ and $\mathbf{a}-\mathbf{b}$ are mutually orthogonal, (ii) calculate the acute angle between the vectors $2\mathbf{a}+\mathbf{b}$ and $\mathbf{a}+2\mathbf{b}$, (iii) obtain a unit vector orthogonal to both $\mathbf{a}$ and $\mathbf{b}$.

3. Show that $(\mathbf{a}.\mathbf{b})^2\leqslant \mathbf{a}^2\mathbf{b}^2$ and deduce that

$$(a_ib_i+a_jb_j+a_kb_k)^2\leqslant (a_i^2+a_j^2+a_k^2)(b_i^2+b_j^2+b_k^2).$$

4. Prove that $\mathbf{a}=(\mathbf{a}.\mathbf{i})\mathbf{i}+(\mathbf{a}.\mathbf{j})\mathbf{j}+(\mathbf{a}.\mathbf{k})\mathbf{k}$.

5. Show that the perpendicular bisectors of the sides of a triangle are concurrent. (Hint: use the identity

$$(\mathbf{b}-\mathbf{c}).\{1-\tfrac{1}{2}(\mathbf{b}+\mathbf{c})\}+(\mathbf{c}-\mathbf{a}).\{1-\tfrac{1}{2}(\mathbf{c}+\mathbf{a})\}+(\mathbf{a}-\mathbf{b}).\{1-\tfrac{1}{2}(\mathbf{a}+\mathbf{b})\} = 0.)$$

9 Vector Product

Let $\mathbf{n}$ be the *unit* vector orthogonal to both $\mathbf{a}$ and $\mathbf{b}$ and such that $\mathbf{a}, \mathbf{b}$ and $\mathbf{n}$ form a right-handed system. We define the **vector product** of two vectors $\mathbf{a}$ and $\mathbf{b}$ inclined at an angle θ to one another, where $0 \leqslant \theta \leqslant \pi$, to be the vector $ab \sin \theta \, \mathbf{n}$.

We agree to denote the vector product by $\mathbf{a} \times \mathbf{b}$ and so it is sometimes referred to as the 'cross' product. (Other notations in use are $\mathbf{a} \wedge \mathbf{b}$, $[\mathbf{a}, \mathbf{b}]$ and $\overset{\frown}{\mathbf{a}\,\mathbf{b}}$.) We have

$$\mathbf{a} \times \mathbf{b} = ab \sin \theta \, \mathbf{n}.$$

Since $\mathbf{b}, \mathbf{a}$ and $-\mathbf{n}$ form a right-handed system, it follows that

$$\mathbf{b} \times \mathbf{a} = -ab \sin \theta \, \mathbf{n}$$

and so

$$\mathbf{a} \times \mathbf{b} = -\mathbf{b} \times \mathbf{a}.$$

That is, vector products satisfy an *anti-commutative* law of multiplication.

If $\mathbf{a} \times \mathbf{b} = \mathbf{0}$, then either $a = 0$, $b = 0$ or $\sin \theta = 0$. In the latter case $\theta = 0$ or π and the two vectors are parallel and have the same or opposite senses. Conversely, the vector product of two parallel vectors is the zero vector. As a special case we have $\mathbf{a} \times \mathbf{a} = \mathbf{0}$.

From the definition we have that if $\mathbf{a}.\mathbf{a} = \mathbf{b}.\mathbf{b} = 1$ and $\mathbf{a}.\mathbf{b} = 0$, the vectors $\mathbf{a}, \mathbf{b}$ and $\mathbf{a} \times \mathbf{b}$ form a right-handed system of mutually orthogonal unit vectors.

The fundamental system of vectors $\mathbf{i}, \mathbf{j}$ and $\mathbf{k}$ satisfies the relations

$$\left.\begin{aligned}
\mathbf{i} \times \mathbf{i} = \mathbf{j} \times \mathbf{j} &= \mathbf{k} \times \mathbf{k} = 0, \\
\mathbf{j} \times \mathbf{k} &= -\mathbf{k} \times \mathbf{j} = \mathbf{i}, \\
\mathbf{k} \times \mathbf{i} &= -\mathbf{i} \times \mathbf{k} = \mathbf{j}, \\
\mathbf{i} \times \mathbf{j} &= -\mathbf{j} \times \mathbf{i} = \mathbf{k}.
\end{aligned}\right\} \tag{9.1}$$

If λ is a scalar, we see from the definition that

$$\lambda(\mathbf{a} \times \mathbf{b}) = (\lambda\mathbf{a}) \times \mathbf{b} = \mathbf{a} \times (\lambda\mathbf{b})$$

and so we can write these equivalent expressions in the form $\lambda\mathbf{a} \times \mathbf{b}$.

At this stage we wish to establish the non-trivial relation

$$\mathbf{a} \times (\mathbf{b} + \mathbf{c}) = \mathbf{a} \times \mathbf{b} + \mathbf{a} \times \mathbf{c}.$$

As a first step let $\boldsymbol{\beta}$ (Fig. 15) be the projected vector of $\mathbf{b}$ on a plane p perpendicular to $\mathbf{a}$. We have $\beta = b \sin \theta$ and so

$$\mathbf{a} \times \mathbf{b} = \mathbf{a} \times \boldsymbol{\beta}.$$

Now let γ be the projected vector of $\mathbf{c}$ on the plane p. Then $\beta+\gamma$ is the projected vector of $\mathbf{b}+\mathbf{c}$ on the plane p. Hence

$$\mathbf{a}\times\mathbf{c} = \mathbf{a}\times\gamma$$

and

$$\mathbf{a}\times(\mathbf{b}+\mathbf{c}) = \mathbf{a}\times(\beta+\gamma).$$

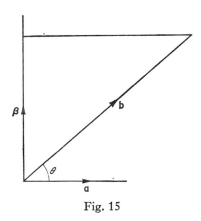

Fig. 15

Since $\mathbf{a}$ is orthogonal to β, it follows that $\mathbf{a}\times\beta$ is a vector in the plane p with magnitude $a\beta$ in a direction orthogonal to β. That is, $\mathbf{a}\times\beta$ is obtained by rotating the vector $a\beta$ through a right-angle in the plane p. Similarly $\mathbf{a}\times\gamma$ is the vector obtained by rotating the vector $a\gamma$ in the plane p through a right-angle in the same sense as the previous rotation. Thus $\mathbf{a}\times\beta+\mathbf{a}\times\gamma$ is the sum of the two vectors $a\beta$ and $a\gamma$ followed by the appropriate rotation in the plane p through a right-angle. This sum $a(\beta+\gamma)$ rotated through a right-angle in the plane p is the vector $\mathbf{a}\times(\beta+\gamma)$ and so

$$\mathbf{a}\times(\beta+\gamma) = \mathbf{a}\times\beta+\mathbf{a}\times\gamma.$$

Accordingly, we have

$$\mathbf{a}\times(\mathbf{b}+\mathbf{c}) = \mathbf{a}\times\mathbf{b}+\mathbf{a}\times\mathbf{c}.$$

As a consequence we may remove brackets as in ordinary algebraic multiplication. That is, vector multiplication is *distributive* with respect to addition.

Let the vectors $\mathbf{a}$ and $\mathbf{b}$ have components a_i, a_j, a_k and b_i, b_j, b_k with respect to a fundamental system $\mathbf{i}$, $\mathbf{j}$ and $\mathbf{k}$. Then

$$\mathbf{a}\times\mathbf{b} = (a_i\mathbf{i}+a_j\mathbf{j}+a_k\mathbf{k})\times(b_i\mathbf{i}+b_j\mathbf{j}+b_k\mathbf{k}).$$

Removal of brackets and use of the vector product properties (9.1) of the vectors of the fundamental system yield

$$\mathbf{a} \times \mathbf{b} = (a_j b_k - a_k b_j)\mathbf{i} + (a_k b_i - a_i b_k)\mathbf{j} + (a_i b_j - a_j b_i)\mathbf{k}. \qquad (9.2)$$

This expression may be written in the determinantal form

$$\begin{vmatrix} a_i & a_j & a_k \\ b_i & b_j & b_k \\ \mathbf{i} & \mathbf{j} & \mathbf{k} \end{vmatrix}.$$

Example. Let A, B and C be given by the vectors $\mathbf{a}$, $\mathbf{b}$ and $\mathbf{c}$. Show that $\frac{1}{2}(\mathbf{b} \times \mathbf{c} + \mathbf{c} \times \mathbf{a} + \mathbf{a} \times \mathbf{b})$ is a vector orthogonal to the triangle ABC with magnitude equal to the area of the triangle.

The vectors $\overrightarrow{AB}$ and $\overrightarrow{AC}$ are given by $\mathbf{b} - \mathbf{a}$ and $\mathbf{c} - \mathbf{a}$. Hence the required vector is $\frac{1}{2}(\mathbf{b} - \mathbf{a}) \times (\mathbf{c} - \mathbf{a})$ from which the required result follows.

EXERCISES

1. Prove that $(\mathbf{a} \times \mathbf{b})^2 = \mathbf{a}^2 \mathbf{b}^2 - (\mathbf{a} . \mathbf{b})^2$.

2. Given $\mathbf{a} = 2\mathbf{i} - 3\mathbf{j} + \mathbf{k}$, $\mathbf{b} = -\mathbf{i} + \mathbf{k}$ and $\mathbf{c} = 2\mathbf{j} - \mathbf{k}$, (i) calculate $\mathbf{a} \times \mathbf{b}$, $\mathbf{b} \times \mathbf{c}$ and $\mathbf{c} \times \mathbf{a}$ in terms of $\mathbf{i}$, $\mathbf{j}$ and $\mathbf{k}$, (ii) obtain a unit vector orthogonal to both $\mathbf{b}$ and $\mathbf{c}$, (iii) calculate the area of the parallelogram with the diagonals $\mathbf{a} + \mathbf{b}$ and $\mathbf{b} + \mathbf{c}$.

3. Given $\mathbf{a} . \mathbf{b} = \mathbf{a} . \mathbf{c}$, $\mathbf{a} \times \mathbf{b} = \mathbf{a} \times \mathbf{c}$ and $\mathbf{a}$ is not the zero vector, show that $\mathbf{b} = \mathbf{c}$.

4. Let $\mathbf{a}$, $\mathbf{b}$ and $\mathbf{c}$ represent the vectors $\overrightarrow{BC}$, $\overrightarrow{CA}$ and $\overrightarrow{AB}$ respectively. Show that $\mathbf{a} \times \mathbf{b} = \mathbf{b} \times \mathbf{c} = \mathbf{c} \times \mathbf{a}$ and deduce the sine rule for a triangle.

10 Scalar Triple Product

We now consider $\mathbf{a} . \mathbf{b} \times \mathbf{c}$. There is no ambiguity in this expression as the vector product $\mathbf{b} \times \mathbf{c}$ must be evaluated and the scalar product of this vector then taken with $\mathbf{a}$. The result is called the **scalar triple product** of the three vectors.

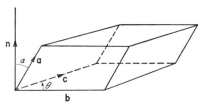

Fig. 16

The vector $\mathbf{b} \times \mathbf{c}$ is the vector $bc \sin \theta \, \mathbf{n}$ where θ is the angle $(0 \leqslant \theta \leqslant \pi)$ between $\mathbf{b}$ and $\mathbf{c}$, and $\mathbf{n}$ is the unit vector orthogonal to both $\mathbf{b}$ and $\mathbf{c}$ such that $\mathbf{b}$, $\mathbf{c}$, and $\mathbf{n}$ form a right-handed system (Fig. 16). The magnitude $bc \sin \theta$ of the vector $\mathbf{b} \times \mathbf{c}$ can be interpreted geometrically as the area of the parallelogram formed by $\mathbf{b}$ and $\mathbf{c}$. Let α be the angle $(0 \leqslant \alpha \leqslant \pi)$ between the vectors $\mathbf{a}$ and $\mathbf{n}$. Then $\mathbf{a} . \mathbf{b} \times \mathbf{c} = abc \sin \theta \cos \alpha$.

The volume of the parallelepiped formed by the three vectors $\mathbf{a}$, $\mathbf{b}$ and $\mathbf{c}$ is equal to the product of the area of the parallelogram formed by $\mathbf{b}$ and $\mathbf{c}$ with the height of the parallelepiped. This height is the component of $\mathbf{a}$ in the direction $\mathbf{n}$ and so is $a \cos \alpha$. Accordingly, the volume of the parallelepiped is $abc \sin \theta \cos \alpha$.

That is, the scalar triple product $\mathbf{a} . \mathbf{b} \times \mathbf{c}$ equals the volume of the parallelepiped formed by the three vectors when set off from a common point.

If $\mathbf{a} . \mathbf{b} \times \mathbf{c}$ is positive, $\cos \alpha$ is positive and so α is acute. Hence $\mathbf{n}$ and $\mathbf{a}$ extend on the same side of the plane formed by $\mathbf{b}$ and $\mathbf{c}$. However, if $\mathbf{a} . \mathbf{b} \times \mathbf{c}$ is negative, α lies between $\pi/2$ and π and so $\mathbf{n}$ and $\mathbf{a}$ extend on opposite sides of this plane.

We extend the definition of right- and left-handedness to non-orthogonal sets of three vectors thus: the vectors $\mathbf{a}$, $\mathbf{b}$ and $\mathbf{c}$ are right-handed (left-handed) if $\mathbf{a}$ and $\mathbf{n}$ are on the same side (opposite sides) of the plane formed by $\mathbf{b}$ and $\mathbf{c}$. The reader is asked to verify that when $\mathbf{a}$, $\mathbf{b}$ and $\mathbf{c}$ are mutually orthogonal, this definition coincides with that of Section 7.

That is, $\mathbf{a}$, $\mathbf{b}$ and $\mathbf{c}$ form a right-handed or a left-handed system according as $\mathbf{a} . \mathbf{b} \times \mathbf{c}$ is positive or negative respectively.

By a similar argument the volume of the parallelepiped is given by $\mathbf{b} . \mathbf{c} \times \mathbf{a}$ and $\mathbf{c} . \mathbf{a} \times \mathbf{b}$ and these triple products are positive or negative according as $\mathbf{a}$, $\mathbf{b}$ and $\mathbf{c}$ form a right-handed or left-handed system respectively. Hence we have

$$\mathbf{a} . \mathbf{b} \times \mathbf{c} = \mathbf{b} . \mathbf{c} \times \mathbf{a} = \mathbf{c} . \mathbf{a} \times \mathbf{b}.$$

Since $\mathbf{c} . \mathbf{a} \times \mathbf{b} = \mathbf{a} \times \mathbf{b} . \mathbf{c}$, it follows that

$$\mathbf{a} . \mathbf{b} \times \mathbf{c} = \mathbf{a} \times \mathbf{b} . \mathbf{c}.$$

That is, we may interchange the dot and cross in a scalar triple product.

Further, we see from the left-handed or right-handed properties that

$$\mathbf{a} . \mathbf{b} \times \mathbf{c} = -\mathbf{b} . \mathbf{a} \times \mathbf{c}.$$

The reader is asked to verify that in all cases the scalar triple product of $\mathbf{a}$, $\mathbf{b}$ and $\mathbf{c}$ taken in the cyclic order $\mathbf{a}$, $\mathbf{b}$, $\mathbf{c}$ equals $\mathbf{a}.\mathbf{b}\times\mathbf{c}$ but equals $-\mathbf{a}.\mathbf{b}\times\mathbf{c}$ for any anti-cyclic order of the vectors.

From the geometrical interpretation it follows that the scalar triple product $\mathbf{a}.\mathbf{b}\times\mathbf{c}$ vanishes if one of the vectors is the zero vector or the three vectors $\mathbf{a}$, $\mathbf{b}$ and $\mathbf{c}$ are coplanar.

Conversely, let the three non-vanishing vectors $\mathbf{a}$, $\mathbf{b}$ and $\mathbf{c}$ satisfy the relation $\mathbf{a}.\mathbf{b}\times\mathbf{c}=0$. Then $\mathbf{a}$ is orthogonal to $\mathbf{b}\times\mathbf{c}$. But by the definition of a vector product, both $\mathbf{b}$ and $\mathbf{c}$ are orthogonal to $\mathbf{b}\times\mathbf{c}$ and so $\mathbf{a}$, $\mathbf{b}$ and $\mathbf{c}$ are all orthogonal to $\mathbf{b}\times\mathbf{c}$. Accordingly $\mathbf{a}$, $\mathbf{b}$ and $\mathbf{c}$ are coplanar vectors.

Let $\mathbf{a}$, $\mathbf{b}$ and $\mathbf{c}$ have components a_i, a_j, a_k; b_i, b_j, b_k and c_i, c_j, c_k respectively with reference to the fundamental system $\mathbf{i}$, $\mathbf{j}$ and $\mathbf{k}$. Then by (9.2) we have

$$\mathbf{b}\times\mathbf{c} = (b_jc_k-b_kc_j)\mathbf{i}+(b_kc_i-b_ic_k)\mathbf{j}+(b_ic_j-b_jc_i)\mathbf{k}$$

and so

$$\mathbf{a}.\mathbf{b}\times\mathbf{c} = a_i(b_jc_k-b_kc_j)+a_j(b_kc_i-b_ic_k)+a_k(b_ic_j-b_jc_i).$$

This result may be written in the determinantal form

$$\mathbf{a}.\mathbf{b}\times\mathbf{c} = \begin{vmatrix} a_i & a_j & a_k \\ b_i & b_j & b_k \\ c_i & c_j & c_k \end{vmatrix}.$$

We agree to use the notation

$$[\mathbf{abc}] = \mathbf{a}.\mathbf{b}\times\mathbf{c}.$$

We note that the vectors of a fundamental system satisfy the relations

$$[\mathbf{ijk}] = [\mathbf{jki}] = [\mathbf{kij}] = 1,$$
$$[\mathbf{ikj}] = [\mathbf{kji}] = [\mathbf{jik}] = -1.$$

EXERCISES

1. Obtain the value of λ which makes the vectors $\mathbf{i}-\mathbf{j}+\mathbf{k}$, $2\mathbf{i}+\mathbf{j}-\mathbf{k}$ and $\lambda\mathbf{i}-\mathbf{j}+\lambda\mathbf{k}$ coplanar.

2. If $\mathbf{a}$, $\mathbf{b}$ and $\mathbf{c}$ are orthogonal vectors, show that

$$[\mathbf{abc}]^2 = \mathbf{a}^2\mathbf{b}^2\mathbf{c}^2.$$

3. Show that

$$(\mathbf{a}+\mathbf{b}).(\mathbf{b}+\mathbf{c})\times(\mathbf{c}+\mathbf{a}) = 2[\mathbf{abc}].$$

11 Vector Triple Product

Consider the vector triple product $\mathbf{a}\times(\mathbf{b}\times\mathbf{c})$. This vector is orthogonal to both $\mathbf{a}$ and $\mathbf{b}\times\mathbf{c}$. But $\mathbf{b}\times\mathbf{c}$ is orthogonal to both $\mathbf{b}$ and

c. It follows that the vector $\mathbf{a} \times (\mathbf{b} \times \mathbf{c})$ lies in the plane of $\mathbf{b}$ and $\mathbf{c}$ and so we may write

$$\mathbf{a} \times (\mathbf{b} \times \mathbf{c}) = \lambda \mathbf{b} + \mu \mathbf{c}.$$

Since $\mathbf{a} \times (\mathbf{b} \times \mathbf{c})$ is orthogonal to $\mathbf{a}$, its scalar product with $\mathbf{a}$ is zero and so

$$\lambda \mathbf{a} . \mathbf{b} + \mu \mathbf{a} . \mathbf{c} = 0.$$

Accordingly we may write

$$\lambda = \rho \mathbf{a} . \mathbf{c}, \qquad \mu = -\rho \mathbf{a} . \mathbf{b},$$

where ρ is still undetermined. Thus we have

$$\mathbf{a} \times (\mathbf{b} \times \mathbf{c}) = \rho [\mathbf{a} . \mathbf{c} \, \mathbf{b} - \mathbf{a} . \mathbf{b} \, \mathbf{c}]. \tag{1}$$

First we consider the case when $\mathbf{a} = \mathbf{b}$ and take the scalar product of both sides of this equation with $\mathbf{c}$ to obtain

$$\mathbf{c} . \mathbf{b} \times (\mathbf{b} \times \mathbf{c}) = \rho [(\mathbf{b} . \mathbf{c})^2 - b^2 c^2].$$

Interchanging the dot and the cross of the scalar triple product we have

$$-(\mathbf{b} \times \mathbf{c})^2 = \rho [(\mathbf{b} . \mathbf{c})^2 - b^2 c^2].$$

Let the angle between $\mathbf{b}$ and $\mathbf{c}$ be φ. Then this equation yields

$$-b^2 c^2 \sin^2 \varphi = \rho [b^2 c^2 \cos^2 \varphi - b^2 c^2],$$

from which $\rho = 1$ in this special case. That is,

$$\mathbf{b} \times (\mathbf{b} \times \mathbf{c}) = \mathbf{b} . \mathbf{c} \, \mathbf{b} - b^2 \mathbf{c}. \tag{2}$$

Now return to the general case when $\mathbf{a}$ and $\mathbf{b}$ differ and take the scalar product of both sides of equation (1) with $\mathbf{b}$ to obtain

$$\mathbf{b} . \mathbf{a} \times (\mathbf{b} \times \mathbf{c}) = \rho [\mathbf{a} . \mathbf{c} \, b^2 - \mathbf{a} . \mathbf{b} \, \mathbf{b} . \mathbf{c}].$$

Interchange of the cyclic order of $\mathbf{b}$, $\mathbf{a}$ and $\mathbf{b} \times \mathbf{c}$ followed by substitution from equation (2) yields

$$-\mathbf{a} . [\mathbf{b} . \mathbf{c} \, \mathbf{b} - b^2 \mathbf{c}] = \rho [\mathbf{a} . \mathbf{c} \, b^2 - \mathbf{a} . \mathbf{b} \, \mathbf{b} . \mathbf{c}],$$

from which we see that ρ is also unity in the general case. That is,

$$\mathbf{a} \times (\mathbf{b} \times \mathbf{c}) = \mathbf{a} . \mathbf{c} \, \mathbf{b} - \mathbf{a} . \mathbf{b} \, \mathbf{c}. \tag{11.1}$$

Note carefully that $(\mathbf{a} \times \mathbf{b}) \times \mathbf{c}$ is not in general the same vector as $\mathbf{a} \times (\mathbf{b} \times \mathbf{c})$ because $(\mathbf{a} \times \mathbf{b}) \times \mathbf{c}$ is a vector in the plane of $\mathbf{a}$ and $\mathbf{b}$. Accordingly it is essential to retain brackets in a vector triple product. We have

$$(\mathbf{a} \times \mathbf{b}) \times \mathbf{c} = -\mathbf{c} \times (\mathbf{a} \times \mathbf{b})$$
$$= \mathbf{a} . \mathbf{c} \, \mathbf{b} - \mathbf{b} . \mathbf{c} \, \mathbf{a}.$$

1. Establish the formula for $\mathbf{a} \times (\mathbf{b} \times \mathbf{c})$ by introducing the components of the vectors with respect to a fundamental system of vectors.

2. Show that $\mathbf{i} \times (\mathbf{j} \times \mathbf{k}) = \mathbf{0}$.

3. If $\mathbf{a} = \mathbf{i} + 2\mathbf{j} - 3\mathbf{k}$, $\mathbf{b} = 2\mathbf{i} - \mathbf{j} + \mathbf{k}$ and $\mathbf{c} = -\mathbf{i} + 4\mathbf{j} - \mathbf{k}$, calculate (i) $\mathbf{a} . \mathbf{b} \times \mathbf{c}$, (ii) $(\mathbf{a} \times \mathbf{b}) \times \mathbf{c}$, (iii) $\mathbf{b} \times (\mathbf{a} \times \mathbf{c})$, (iv) $(\mathbf{a} \times \mathbf{b}) \times (\mathbf{c} \times \mathbf{a})$, (v) $[\mathbf{a} \times \mathbf{b} \quad \mathbf{b} \times \mathbf{c} \quad \mathbf{c} \times \mathbf{a}]$, (vi) $(\mathbf{a} \times \mathbf{b}) \times \{(\mathbf{b} \times \mathbf{c}) \times (\mathbf{c} \times \mathbf{a})\}$.

4. Show that $\mathbf{a} \times (\mathbf{b} \times \mathbf{c}) = (\mathbf{a} \times \mathbf{b}) \times \mathbf{c}$ if and only if $\mathbf{b} = \mathbf{0}$ or $\mathbf{c}$ is parallel to $\mathbf{a}$ or $\mathbf{b}$ is orthogonal to both $\mathbf{c}$ and $\mathbf{a}$.

5. If $\mathbf{a}$ is not the zero vector, prove that every solution of the equation $\mathbf{a} \times \mathbf{x} = \mathbf{b}$ is given by $\mathbf{x} = (\mathbf{b} \times \mathbf{a})/a^2 + \lambda\mathbf{a}$, where λ is an arbitrary scalar.

12   Products of Four Vectors

There is no ambiguity in the expression $\mathbf{a} \times \mathbf{b} . \mathbf{c} \times \mathbf{d}$ as the two vector products must be formed before the scalar product can be evaluated. The interchange of dot and cross yields

$$\begin{aligned}
\mathbf{a} \times \mathbf{b} . \mathbf{c} \times \mathbf{d} &= \mathbf{a} . \mathbf{b} \times (\mathbf{c} \times \mathbf{d}) \\
&= \mathbf{a} . (\mathbf{b} . \mathbf{dc} - \mathbf{b} . \mathbf{cd}) \\
&= \mathbf{a} . \mathbf{c} \, \mathbf{b} . \mathbf{d} - \mathbf{a} . \mathbf{d} \, \mathbf{b} . \mathbf{c}.
\end{aligned} \tag{12.1}$$

In particular, choose $\mathbf{c} = \mathbf{a}$ and $\mathbf{d} = \mathbf{b}$ to obtain

$$(\mathbf{a} \times \mathbf{b})^2 = a^2 b^2 - (\mathbf{a} . \mathbf{b})^2. \tag{12.2}$$

Next let us consider $(\mathbf{a} \times \mathbf{b}) \times (\mathbf{c} \times \mathbf{d})$ and evaluate as the vector triple product $\boldsymbol{\alpha} \times (\mathbf{c} \times \mathbf{d})$, where $\boldsymbol{\alpha} = \mathbf{a} \times \mathbf{b}$. The result is

$$(\mathbf{a} \times \mathbf{b}) \times (\mathbf{c} \times \mathbf{d}) = [\mathbf{abd}]\mathbf{c} - [\mathbf{abc}]\mathbf{d}.$$

The calculation can also be made from $(\mathbf{a} \times \mathbf{b}) \times \boldsymbol{\beta}$, where $\boldsymbol{\beta} = \mathbf{c} \times \mathbf{d}$ with the result

$$(\mathbf{a} \times \mathbf{b}) \times (\mathbf{c} \times \mathbf{d}) = [\mathbf{cda}]\mathbf{b} - [\mathbf{cdb}]\mathbf{a}.$$

Equate the two expressions for $(\mathbf{a} \times \mathbf{b}) \times (\mathbf{c} \times \mathbf{d})$; then solve for $\mathbf{d}$, provided that $[\mathbf{abc}]$ is not zero, to obtain

$$\mathbf{d} = \frac{[\mathbf{bcd}]\mathbf{a} + [\mathbf{cad}]\mathbf{b} + [\mathbf{abd}]\mathbf{c}}{[\mathbf{abc}]}. \tag{12.3}$$

This relation shows how any vector $\mathbf{d}$ can be expressed as a linear combination of any three given non-coplanar vectors $\mathbf{a}$, $\mathbf{b}$ and $\mathbf{c}$. That is, any four vectors are always linearly dependent.

1. Prove
   (i) $\mathbf{a} \times (\mathbf{b} \times \mathbf{c}) + \mathbf{b} \times (\mathbf{c} \times \mathbf{a}) + \mathbf{c} \times (\mathbf{a} \times \mathbf{b}) = \mathbf{0}$

(ii) $[\mathbf{b} \times \mathbf{c} \quad \mathbf{c} \times \mathbf{a} \quad \mathbf{a} \times \mathbf{b}] = [\mathbf{abc}]^2,$

(iii) $(\mathbf{b} \times \mathbf{c}) \times (\mathbf{a} \times \mathbf{d}) + (\mathbf{c} \times \mathbf{a}) \times (\mathbf{b} \times \mathbf{d}) + (\mathbf{a} \times \mathbf{b}) \times (\mathbf{c} \times \mathbf{d}) = -2[\mathbf{abc}]\mathbf{d},$

(iv) $\mathbf{b} \times \mathbf{c} . \mathbf{a} \times \mathbf{d} + \mathbf{c} \times \mathbf{a} . \mathbf{b} \times \mathbf{d} + \mathbf{a} \times \mathbf{b} . \mathbf{c} \times \mathbf{d} = 0,$

(v) $\mathbf{b} \times \mathbf{c}\mathbf{a} . \mathbf{d} + \mathbf{c} \times \mathbf{a}\mathbf{b} . \mathbf{d} + \mathbf{a} \times \mathbf{b}\mathbf{c} . \mathbf{d} = [\mathbf{abc}]\mathbf{d}.$

2. The *unit* vectors $\mathbf{a}$, $\mathbf{b}$ and $\mathbf{c}$ define a spherical triangle ABC on a unit sphere with centre at the origin O. Let α, β and γ denote the arcs of the great circles forming the triangle, labelled so that α is opposite to the angle at A, etc. Show that $(\mathbf{a} \times \mathbf{b}) \times (\mathbf{a} \times \mathbf{c}) = [\mathbf{abc}]\mathbf{a}$ and deduce that $\sin \alpha \sin \beta \sin C = [\mathbf{abc}]$. Hence obtain

$$\frac{\sin A}{\sin \alpha} = \frac{\sin B}{\sin \beta} = \frac{\sin C}{\sin \gamma}.$$

This relations is known as the **sine law for spherical triangles.**

13 Reciprocal Basis

A set of three non-coplanar vectors $\mathbf{e}_1$, $\mathbf{e}_2$ and $\mathbf{e}_3$ is called a **basis** because any vector can be expressed linearly in terms of any three non-coplanar vectors by equation (12.3). The basis is said to be right-handed or left-handed according as $[\mathbf{e}_1\mathbf{e}_2\mathbf{e}_3]$ is positive or negative.

A second basis $\mathbf{e}^1$, $\mathbf{e}^2$ and $\mathbf{e}^3$† is said to be **reciprocal** to $\mathbf{e}_1$, $\mathbf{e}_2$ and $\mathbf{e}_3$ if

$$\left.\begin{array}{lll} \mathbf{e}_1 . \mathbf{e}^1 = 1, & \mathbf{e}_1 . \mathbf{e}^2 = 0, & \mathbf{e}_1 . \mathbf{e}^3 = 0, \\ \mathbf{e}_2 . \mathbf{e}^1 = 0, & \mathbf{e}_2 . \mathbf{e}^2 = 1, & \mathbf{e}_2 . \mathbf{e}^3 = 0, \\ \mathbf{e}_3 . \mathbf{e}^1 = 0, & \mathbf{e}_3 . \mathbf{e}^2 = 0, & \mathbf{e}_3 . \mathbf{e}^3 = 1. \end{array}\right\} \quad (13.1)$$

The vector $\mathbf{e}^1$ is orthogonal to both $\mathbf{e}_2$ and $\mathbf{e}_3$ and so we may write $\mathbf{e}^1 = \lambda\mathbf{e}_2 \times \mathbf{e}_3$. Substitution in $\mathbf{e}_1 . \mathbf{e}^1 = 1$ yields $\lambda[\mathbf{e}_1\mathbf{e}_2\mathbf{e}_3] = 1$. Hence we have

$$\mathbf{e}^1 = \frac{\mathbf{e}_2 \times \mathbf{e}_3}{[\mathbf{e}_1\mathbf{e}_2\mathbf{e}_3]}, \quad \mathbf{e}^2 = \frac{\mathbf{e}_3 \times \mathbf{e}_1}{[\mathbf{e}_1\mathbf{e}_2\mathbf{e}_3]}, \quad \mathbf{e}^3 = \frac{\mathbf{e}_1 \times \mathbf{e}_2}{[\mathbf{e}_1\mathbf{e}_2\mathbf{e}_3]}. \quad (13.2)$$

From the relative symmetry in $\mathbf{e}_1$, $\mathbf{e}_2$, $\mathbf{e}_3$ and $\mathbf{e}^1$, $\mathbf{e}^2$, $\mathbf{e}^3$ we have similarly that

$$\mathbf{e}_1 = \frac{\mathbf{e}^2 \times \mathbf{e}^3}{[\mathbf{e}^1\mathbf{e}^2\mathbf{e}^3]}, \quad \mathbf{e}_2 = \frac{\mathbf{e}^3 \times \mathbf{e}^1}{[\mathbf{e}^1\mathbf{e}^2\mathbf{e}^3]}, \quad \mathbf{e}_3 = \frac{\mathbf{e}^1 \times \mathbf{e}^2}{[\mathbf{e}^1\mathbf{e}^2\mathbf{e}^3]}. \quad (13.3)$$

EXERCISES

1. Obtain a set of vectors reciprocal to the three vectors $-\mathbf{i}+\mathbf{j}+\mathbf{k}$, $\mathbf{i}-\mathbf{j}+\mathbf{k}$ and $\mathbf{i}+\mathbf{j}-\mathbf{k}$.

† The indices 1, 2 and 3 of $\mathbf{e}^1$, $\mathbf{e}^2$ and $\mathbf{e}^3$ merely serve as distinguishing 'labels' and do not possess any significance as power indices.

2. If e_1, e_2 e_3 form a self-reciprocal basis, show that they are the unit vectors of a fundamental system.

3. Prove that (i) $[e_1e_2e_3][e^1e^2e^3]=1$,

$$\text{(ii) } e_1\times e^1+e_2\times e^2+e_3\times e^3=0,$$
$$\text{(iii) } [e_1e_2e_3]^3[e^1e^2e^3]=[e_2\times e_3 \; e_3\times e_1 \; e_1\times e_2].$$

MISCELLANEOUS EXERCISES

1. If $b\times c$ is not the zero vector, obtain x in terms of a, b and c given that $a.x=1$, $b.x=0$ and $c.x=0$.

2. If a, b and c are three non-coplanar vectors, show that the vectors $b\times c$, $c\times a$ and $a\times b$ are non-coplanar and prove that any vector d can be expressed in the form

$$d = \{a.db\times c+b.dc\times a+c.da\times b\}/[abc].$$

3. Show that the internal bisector of an angle of a triangle divides the opposite side in the ratio of the other two sides. Deduce that the internal bisectors of the angles of a triangle are concurrent.

4. The coplanar straight lines AL, BM and CN are concurrent. Prove that the points of intersection of AB and LM, BC and MN, CA and NL are collinear.

5. Show that the mid-points of the diagonals of a complete quadrilateral are collinear.

6. Show that the sum of the four vectors of magnitudes equal to the areas of the faces of a tetrahedron and directed outwards perpendicular to the faces is zero.

Generalize this result to a closed polyhedron.

7. If the vector triple e^1, e^2, e^3 is reciprocal to the triple e_1, e_2, e_3, show that any vector a satisfies the relation

$$a = (a.e^1)e_1+(a.e^2)e_2+(a.e^3)e_3$$
and
$$a = (a.e_1)e^1+(a.e_2)e^2+(a.e_3)e^3.$$

8. Show that $(a\times b)\cdot(a\times c)=(b.c)(a.a)-(a.c)(a.b)$. Hence, with the notation of exercise 2, page 21, deduce the **cosine law for spherical triangles**

$$\cos\alpha = \cos\beta\cos\gamma+\sin\beta\sin\gamma\cos A.$$

9. Obtain the angle (a) between two faces, (b) between a face and an edge which intersects it, of a regular tetrahedron.

10. D, E and F are points on the sides BC, CA and AB of a triangle ABC such that AD, BE and CF are concurrent. Use vector methods to prove **Ceva's** theorem that

$$\frac{BD}{DC}\cdot\frac{CE}{EA}\cdot\frac{AF}{FB} = 1.$$

CHAPTER 2

Applications to Space Geometry†

In this chapter vectors are used in two different ways. Firstly, the position of a point in space is denoted by a vector whose initial point is *fixed*. The other end of the vector determines the point uniquely in space. Such vectors will be denoted by bold Roman letters. Secondly, a vector may merely determine a direction in space irrespective of its initial point. Such vectors will be denoted by bold Greek letters.

14   Straight Line

There is a unique straight line (Fig. 17) through A, given by the vector **a** referred to some fixed initial point O, called the **origin**, in the direction of the vector **α**. Let **r** be the position vector of any point

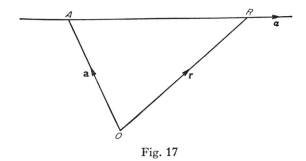

Fig. 17

R on this straight line. From $\overrightarrow{OR} = \overrightarrow{OA} + \overrightarrow{AR}$ we have

$$\mathbf{r} = \mathbf{a} + u\boldsymbol{\alpha}$$

† The content of this chapter is not required for the understanding of the remainder of the text.

where the value of the parameter u depends on the position of R on the straight line. As u varies from $-\infty$ to $+\infty$ the point R traces out every point of the straight line.

We have $\overrightarrow{AR} = \mathbf{r} - \mathbf{a}$ and so $AR^2 = (\mathbf{r} - \mathbf{a})^2 = u^2 \alpha^2$. Accordingly, u measures the actual distance AR if and only if $\boldsymbol{\alpha}$ is chosen to be a *unit* vector.

The parameter u can be eliminated from the equation $\mathbf{r} = \mathbf{a} + u\boldsymbol{\alpha}$ by writing it in the equivalent form

$$(\mathbf{r} - \mathbf{a}) \times \boldsymbol{\alpha} = \mathbf{0}.$$

Next we calculate the perpendicular distance (Fig. 18) BM from B, given by the vector $\mathbf{b}$, to the straight line $\mathbf{r} = \mathbf{a} + u\boldsymbol{\alpha}$. We have $\overrightarrow{AB} = \mathbf{b} - \mathbf{a}$ and $|\overrightarrow{AB} \times \boldsymbol{\alpha}| = \alpha AB \sin \theta = \alpha BM$, where θ is the angle BAM.

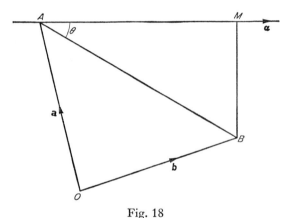

Fig. 18

Accordingly,

$$BM^2 = \{(\mathbf{a} - \mathbf{b}) \times \boldsymbol{\alpha}\}^2 / \alpha^2.$$

An alternative method yields

$$BM^2 = AB^2 - AM^2$$
$$= (\mathbf{a} - \mathbf{b})^2 - \{(\mathbf{a} - \mathbf{b}) . \boldsymbol{\alpha} / \alpha\}^2$$
$$= \frac{(\mathbf{a} - \mathbf{b})^2 \alpha^2 - \{(\mathbf{a} - \mathbf{b}) . \boldsymbol{\alpha}\}^2}{\alpha^2}.$$

The equality of the two expressions for BM^2 is verified from equation (12.2).

Example. Show that if the two straight lines $\mathbf{r} = \mathbf{a} + u\boldsymbol{\alpha}$ and $\mathbf{r} = \mathbf{b} + v\boldsymbol{\beta}$ intersect then $(\mathbf{a} - \mathbf{b}) . \boldsymbol{\alpha} \times \boldsymbol{\beta} = 0$ but $\boldsymbol{\alpha} \times \boldsymbol{\beta} \neq \mathbf{0}$.

If the straight lines intersect, values of u and v exist for which $\mathbf{a}+u\boldsymbol{\alpha}=\mathbf{b}+v\boldsymbol{\beta}$. The required result is obtained by taking the scalar product with $\boldsymbol{\alpha}\times\boldsymbol{\beta}$. Note that the vanishing of $\boldsymbol{\alpha}\times\boldsymbol{\beta}$ implies that the straight lines are parallel.

15 Plane

Consider the plane (Fig. 19) through A, given by the vector $\mathbf{a}$, containing the directions given by the vectors $\boldsymbol{\alpha}$ and $\boldsymbol{\beta}$. By the parallelogram law of addition of vectors, the vector AR corresponding

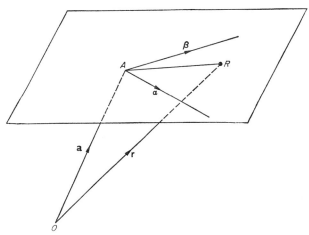

Fig. 19

to any point R on the plane of $\boldsymbol{\alpha}$ and $\boldsymbol{\beta}$ is given by $u\boldsymbol{\alpha}+v\boldsymbol{\beta}$ where u and v are parameters. Then the position vector $\mathbf{r}$ of R is given by

$$\mathbf{r} = \mathbf{a}+u\boldsymbol{\alpha}+v\boldsymbol{\beta}.$$

This equation represents the required plane. To each point R on it there corresponds a pair of values of u and v.

We may eliminate the parameters u and v to obtain the equation of the plane in the form

$$(\mathbf{r}-\mathbf{a}).\boldsymbol{\alpha}\times\boldsymbol{\beta} = 0.$$

This equation can be obtained directly by noting that $\boldsymbol{\alpha}\times\boldsymbol{\beta}$ is a vector orthogonal to the plane and $\mathbf{r}-\mathbf{a}$ is a vector lying in the plane.

The equation of the plane through the three points A, B and C, given respectively by the vectors $\mathbf{a}$, $\mathbf{b}$ and $\mathbf{c}$, is obtained by noting that the vectors $\mathbf{b}-\mathbf{a}$ and $\mathbf{c}-\mathbf{a}$ are parallel to the plane. Hence the equation satisfied by **r**, the position vector of any point R on the plane, is

$$\mathbf{r} = \mathbf{a} + u(\mathbf{b} - \mathbf{a}) + v(\mathbf{c} - \mathbf{a})$$
$$= (1 - u - v)\mathbf{a} + u\mathbf{b} + v\mathbf{c}.$$

That is,

$$\mathbf{r} = \lambda\mathbf{a} + \mu\mathbf{b} + \nu\mathbf{c},$$

where

$$\lambda + \mu + \nu = 1.$$

Next we calculate the perpendicular distance BL (Fig. 20) from B, given by the vector **b**, to the plane $(\mathbf{r} - \mathbf{a}).(\alpha \times \beta) = 0$. We note that

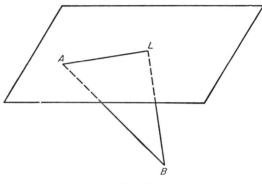

Fig. 20

BL is the component of the vector $\overrightarrow{BA} = \mathbf{a} - \mathbf{b}$ in the direction of $\overrightarrow{BL}$. This direction is parallel to the vector $\alpha \times \beta$. Hence we have

$$BL = \frac{\pm(\mathbf{a} - \mathbf{b}).\alpha \times \beta}{|\alpha \times \beta|}.$$

16   Shortest Distance between Two Skew Lines

Consider (Fig. 21) the two straight lines through A and B, given by the vectors **a** and **b**, in the respective directions α and β. The corresponding equations are $\mathbf{r} = \mathbf{a} + u\alpha$ and $\mathbf{r} = \mathbf{b} + v\beta$. The shortest distance between a point and a straight line is the perpendicular to it from the point. Consequently the shortest distance between two skew lines is along the line which is perpendicular to both of them. That is, the shortest distance between these two straight lines is LM, where LM is perpendicular to both the vectors α and β. Accordingly, the vector

$\alpha \times \beta$ is along $\overrightarrow{LM}$. But LM is the component of the vector $\overrightarrow{AB}$ in the direction of $\overrightarrow{LM}$ and so we have

$$LM = \frac{(\mathbf{a}-\mathbf{b}).\alpha \times \beta}{|\alpha \times \beta|},$$

since $(\alpha \times \beta)/|\alpha \times \beta|$ is a *unit* vector in the direction of $\overrightarrow{LM}$.

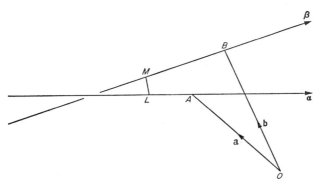

Fig. 21

We deduce that the necessary and sufficient condition that the two straight lines intersect is $(\mathbf{a}-\mathbf{b}).\alpha \times \beta = 0$ provided that $\alpha \times \beta \neq \mathbf{0}$. We note that this condition agrees with the result in Section 14.

MISCELLANEOUS EXERCISES

1. Calculate the perpendicular distance from the point $(-2, 1, 5)$ to the straight line joining the points $(1, 2, -5)$ and $(7, 5, -9)$.
2. Calculate the perpendicular distance from the point $(-2, 3, -1)$ to the plane determined by the three points $(-4, 4, -8)$, $(-5, 8, -11)$ and $(-7, -2, -8)$.
3. Calculate the shortest distance between the straight lines joining the points $(-14, 8, 6)$, $(-11, 4, 1)$ and the points $(3, 5, 5)$, $(6, 11, 8)$.
4. Show that the straight line through the point represented by the vector $\mathbf{b}$ perpendicular to and intersecting the straight line $\mathbf{r}=\mathbf{a}+u\alpha$ is given by $\mathbf{r}=\mathbf{b}+v\alpha \times \{(\mathbf{a}-\mathbf{b}) \times \alpha\}$.
5. Show that the equation of the plane through the points A, B and C given by the vectors $\mathbf{a}$, $\mathbf{b}$ and $\mathbf{c}$ respectively can be written in the symmetrical form

$$(3\mathbf{r}-\mathbf{a}-\mathbf{b}-\mathbf{c}).(\mathbf{b} \times \mathbf{c}+\mathbf{c} \times \mathbf{a}+\mathbf{a} \times \mathbf{b}) = 0.$$

6. Show that the point of intersection of the straight line $(\mathbf{r}-\mathbf{a})\times\mathbf{\alpha}=0$ and the plane $(\mathbf{r}-\mathbf{b}).\mathbf{\beta}=0$ is at the point given by the vector $\mathbf{a}+\lambda\mathbf{\alpha}$, where

$$\lambda = \frac{(\mathbf{b}-\mathbf{a}).\mathbf{\beta}}{\mathbf{\alpha}.\mathbf{\beta}}.$$

7. Show that the line of intersection of the two planes $(\mathbf{r}-\mathbf{a}).\mathbf{\alpha}=0$ and $(\mathbf{r}-\mathbf{b}).\mathbf{\beta}=0$ is given by $(\mathbf{r}-\mathbf{c})\times(\mathbf{\alpha}\times\mathbf{\beta})=0$, where

$$\mathbf{c}(\mathbf{\alpha}\times\mathbf{\beta})^2 = \mathbf{a}.\mathbf{\alpha}[\mathbf{\beta}\times(\mathbf{\alpha}\times\mathbf{\beta})]+\mathbf{b}.\mathbf{\beta}[\mathbf{\alpha}\times(\mathbf{\beta}\times\mathbf{\alpha})].$$

8. The **Plucker** vectors of the straight line through the point A given by the vector $\mathbf{a}$ and parallel to the direction of the vector $\mathbf{\alpha}$ are $\mathbf{p}$ and $\mathbf{q}$, where $\mathbf{p}=\mathbf{\alpha}/|\mathbf{\alpha}|$ and $\mathbf{q}=\mathbf{a}\times\mathbf{p}$. Show that

  (i) $\mathbf{p}$ is independent of the choice of the point A on the straight line,

  (ii) the perpendicular distance from the point given by the vector $\mathbf{b}$ from the straight line is $|\mathbf{p}\times\mathbf{b}+\mathbf{q}|$,

  (iii) the straight lines corresponding to the Plucker vectors $\mathbf{p}_1$, $\mathbf{q}_1$ and $\mathbf{p}_2$, $\mathbf{q}_2$ intersect if and only if $\mathbf{p}_1.\mathbf{q}_2+\mathbf{p}_2.\mathbf{q}_1=0$ and $\mathbf{p}_1\times\mathbf{p}_2\neq0$,

  (iv) the equation of the plane through A and the line with Plucker vectors $\mathbf{p}_1$, $\mathbf{q}_1$ is

$$\mathbf{r}.\mathbf{q}_1-[\mathbf{r}\ \mathbf{a}\ \mathbf{p}_1] = \mathbf{a}.\mathbf{q}_1.$$

CHAPTER 3

Differential Vector Calculus

17 Derivative of a Vector

Let $\mathbf{p}(u)$ denote a vector function of the scalar variable u, where u is restricted to some range of values $u_1 \leqslant u \leqslant u_2$. By this statement we mean that $\mathbf{p}(u)$ is uniquely determined when u is given a value in its range.

As an example consider the vector $\mathbf{p} = \mathbf{a} + u\boldsymbol{\alpha}$. As u varies, $\mathbf{p}$ represents the vectors joining the origin to any point of the straight line through the point† $\mathbf{a}$ in the direction $\boldsymbol{\alpha}$. For this vector, u may range from $-\infty$ to $+\infty$.

The vector function $\mathbf{p}(u)$ is said to be **continuous** at u_0 if, given any positive number ε, it is possible to find another positive number δ such that $|\mathbf{p}(u) - \mathbf{p}(u_0)| < \varepsilon$ when $|u - u_0| < \delta$. This condition is also written in the form $\lim_{u \to u_0} \mathbf{p}(u) = \mathbf{p}(u_0)$.

The **derivative** $\dot{\mathbf{p}}(u)$ is defined by

$$\dot{\mathbf{p}}(u) = \frac{d\mathbf{p}}{du} = \lim_{\Delta u \to 0} \frac{\mathbf{p}(u + \Delta u) - \mathbf{p}(u)}{\Delta u}$$

provided that this limit exists. In this case we also say that $\mathbf{p}(u)$ is **differentiable**. (The dot above the letter will always denote differentiation with respect to u.)

Since $\dot{\mathbf{p}}(u)$ is itself a vector function of u, we can consider its derivative with respect to u. If this derivative exists we denote it by $\ddot{\mathbf{p}}(u)$, where

$$\ddot{\mathbf{p}}(u) = \frac{d}{du}(\dot{\mathbf{p}}(u)) = \frac{d^2\mathbf{p}}{du^2}.$$

Similarly, higher derivatives of any order can be defined.

---

† When the vector $\mathbf{a}$ represents the directed line segment $\overrightarrow{OA}$, where O is the origin, we occasionally refer to A as the *point* $\mathbf{a}$.

Example. Obtain the derivative of the constant vector $\mathbf{c}$. Let $\mathbf{p}(u)=\mathbf{c}$ and so $\mathbf{p}(u+\varDelta u)=\mathbf{c}$ from which $\dot{\mathbf{p}}(u)=0$. That is, the derivative of a constant vector is the zero vector.

18 Derivative of a Sum of Vectors

Divide both sides of the identity

$$\{\mathbf{p}(u+\varDelta u)+\mathbf{q}(u+\varDelta u)\}-\{\mathbf{p}(u)+\mathbf{q}(u)\}$$
$$= \{\mathbf{p}(u+\varDelta u)-\mathbf{p}(u)\}+\{\mathbf{q}(u+\varDelta u)-\mathbf{q}(u)\}$$

by $\varDelta u$ and proceed to the limit as $\varDelta u$ tends to zero. It follows that

$$\frac{d}{du}(\mathbf{p}+\mathbf{q}) = \frac{d\mathbf{p}}{du}+\frac{d\mathbf{q}}{du}.$$

It follows from the commutative and associative laws of addition of vectors that for a finite number n of vectors $\mathbf{p}_i(u)$ we have

$$\frac{d}{du}\left(\sum_{i=1}^{n}\mathbf{p}_i\right) = \sum_{i=1}^{n}\frac{d\mathbf{p}_i}{du}.$$

19 Derivative of the Product of a Scalar and a Vector Function

Consider $\mathbf{p}(u)=f(u)\mathbf{a}(u)$, where $f(u)$ is a scalar function of u and $\mathbf{a}(u)$ is a vector function of u. Then we have

$$\mathbf{p}(u+\varDelta u) = f(u+\varDelta u)\mathbf{a}(u+\varDelta u).$$

Divide both sides of the identity

$$\mathbf{p}(u+\varDelta u)-\mathbf{p}(u)$$
$$= f(u+\varDelta u)\{\mathbf{a}(u+\varDelta u)-\mathbf{a}(u)\}+\{f(u+\varDelta u)-f(u)\}\mathbf{a}(u)$$

by $\varDelta u$ and proceed to the limit as $\varDelta u$ tends to zero. It follows that

$$\frac{d}{du}(f\mathbf{a}) = f\frac{d\mathbf{a}}{du}+\frac{df}{du}\mathbf{a}.$$

EXERCISES

1. If n, $\mathbf{a}$ and $\mathbf{b}$ are constant and $\mathbf{p}=\mathbf{a}\cos nt+\mathbf{b}\sin nt$, prove that

$$\mathbf{p}\times\frac{d\mathbf{p}}{dt} = n\mathbf{a}\times\mathbf{b} \quad\text{and}\quad \frac{d^2\mathbf{p}}{dt^2}+n^2\mathbf{p} = 0.$$

2. Find $\mathbf{p}$ satisfying the equation $\ddot{\mathbf{p}}(u)=\mathbf{a}u+\mathbf{b}$, where $\mathbf{a}$ and $\mathbf{b}$ are constant vectors, given that $\mathbf{p}$ and $\dot{\mathbf{p}}$ both vanish when $u=0$.

3. Show that $\dfrac{d}{du}(\mathbf{p}/p)=\dot{\mathbf{p}}/p-\dot{p}\mathbf{p}/p^2$.

20 Derivative of a Scalar Product

Consider $f(u) = \mathbf{a}(u) . \mathbf{b}(u)$, where $\mathbf{a}$ and $\mathbf{b}$ are vector functions of the scalar u. Then we have $f(u+\Delta u) = \mathbf{a}(u+\Delta u) . \mathbf{b}(u+\Delta u)$. Divide both sides of the identity

$$f(u+\Delta u) - f(u)$$
$$= \mathbf{a}(u+\Delta u) . \{\mathbf{b}(u+\Delta u) - \mathbf{b}(u)\} + \{\mathbf{a}(u+\Delta u) - \mathbf{a}(u)\} . \mathbf{b}(u)$$

by Δu and proceed to the limit as Δu tends to zero. It follows that

$$\frac{d}{du}(\mathbf{a}.\mathbf{b}) = \mathbf{a}.\frac{d\mathbf{b}}{du} + \frac{d\mathbf{a}}{du}.\mathbf{b}.$$

In particular, we have

$$\frac{d}{du}\mathbf{a}^2 = \frac{d}{du}(\mathbf{a}.\mathbf{a}) = 2\mathbf{a}.\frac{d\mathbf{a}}{du}.$$

But $\mathbf{a}^2 = a^2$ and so $\dfrac{d}{du}\mathbf{a}^2 = 2a\dfrac{da}{du}.$ Hence we have

$$\mathbf{a}.\frac{d\mathbf{a}}{du} = a\frac{da}{du}.$$

Further, if $\mathbf{a}$ is a vector of *constant magnitude*, $\dfrac{da}{du} = 0$ and so $\mathbf{a}.\dfrac{d\mathbf{a}}{du} = 0$.

That is, the derivative of a vector of constant magnitude is either orthogonal to it or zero.

21 Derivative of a Vector Product

Consider $\mathbf{p}(u) = \mathbf{a}(u) \times \mathbf{b}(u)$, where $\mathbf{a}$ and $\mathbf{b}$ are vector functions of u. Then $\mathbf{p}(u+\Delta u) = \mathbf{a}(u+\Delta u) \times \mathbf{b}(u+\Delta u)$. Divide both sides of the identity

$$\mathbf{p}(u+\Delta u) - \mathbf{p}(u)$$
$$= \mathbf{a}(u+\Delta u) \times \{\mathbf{b}(u+\Delta u) - \mathbf{b}(u)\} + \{\mathbf{a}(u+\Delta u) - \mathbf{a}(u)\} \times \mathbf{b}(u)$$

by Δu and proceed to the limit as Δu tends to zero. It follows that

$$\frac{d}{du}(\mathbf{a} \times \mathbf{b}) = \mathbf{a} \times \frac{d\mathbf{b}}{du} + \frac{d\mathbf{a}}{du} \times \mathbf{b}.$$

It is important in this case not to interfere with the order of the vectors as vector multiplication is anti-commutative.

We immediately deduce that

$$\frac{d}{du}(\mathbf{a}.\mathbf{b}\times\mathbf{c}) = \dot{\mathbf{a}}.\mathbf{b}\times\mathbf{c}+\mathbf{a}.\frac{d}{du}(\mathbf{b}\times\mathbf{c})$$

$$= \dot{\mathbf{a}}.\mathbf{b}\times\mathbf{c}+\mathbf{a}.\dot{\mathbf{b}}\times\mathbf{c}+\mathbf{a}.\mathbf{b}\times\dot{\mathbf{c}}.$$

Similarly we obtain

$$\frac{d}{du}\{\mathbf{a}\times(\mathbf{b}\times\mathbf{c})\} = \dot{\mathbf{a}}\times(\mathbf{b}\times\mathbf{c})+\mathbf{a}\times(\dot{\mathbf{b}}\times\mathbf{c})+\mathbf{a}\times(\mathbf{b}\times\dot{\mathbf{c}}).$$

EXERCISES

1. Show that (i) $\frac{d}{du}(\mathbf{p}\times\dot{\mathbf{p}})=\mathbf{p}\times\ddot{\mathbf{p}}$, (ii) $\frac{d}{du}[\mathbf{p}\,\dot{\mathbf{p}}\,\ddot{\mathbf{p}}]=[\mathbf{p}\,\dot{\mathbf{p}}\,\dddot{\mathbf{p}}]$.

2. If $\mathbf{a}$ is a unit vector in the direction of $\mathbf{b}$, show that $\mathbf{a}\times\dot{\mathbf{a}}=(\mathbf{b}\times\dot{\mathbf{b}})/(\mathbf{b}.\mathbf{b})$.

3. If $\frac{d\mathbf{a}}{du}=\boldsymbol{\omega}\times\mathbf{a}$ and $\frac{d\mathbf{b}}{du}=\boldsymbol{\omega}\times\mathbf{b}$, show that

$$\frac{d}{du}(\mathbf{a}\times\mathbf{b}) = \boldsymbol{\omega}\times(\mathbf{a}\times\mathbf{b}).$$

4. If $\mathbf{r}\times\frac{d\mathbf{r}}{du}=0$, show that $\mathbf{r}$ has a fixed direction. (Hint: Let $\mathbf{r}=f(u)\mathbf{e}(u)$, where $\mathbf{e}(u)$ is a unit vector. Deduce that $\mathbf{e}\times\dot{\mathbf{e}}=0$ and $\mathbf{e}.\dot{\mathbf{e}}=0$.)

22 Taylor's Theorem for a Vector Function

Suppose that the vector $\mathbf{p}(u)$ and its derivatives up to order $n-1$ are continuous for $a\leqslant u\leqslant a+h$ and $\mathbf{p}^{(n)}(u)$ exists for $a<u<a+h$. Under these conditions we prove **Taylor's theorem** that

$$\mathbf{p}(a+h) = \mathbf{p}(a)+h\mathbf{p}'(a)+\cdots$$
$$+\frac{1}{(n-1)!}h^{n-1}\mathbf{p}^{(n-1)}(a)+\frac{1}{n!}h^n\mathbf{p}^{(n)}(a+\theta h), \qquad (22.1)$$

where $0<\theta<1$.

If, in addition, $\lim_{n\to\infty}\{(h^n/n!)\mathbf{p}^{(n)}(a+\theta h)\}=0$ the vector function $\mathbf{p}(a+h)$ has the **Taylor expansion**

$$\mathbf{p}(a+h) = p(a)+h\mathbf{p}'(a)+\cdots+\frac{1}{n!}h^n\mathbf{p}^{(n)}(a)+\cdots.$$

Define the vector $\mathbf{q}(u)$ for $0\leqslant u\leqslant h$ by

$$\mathbf{q}(u) \equiv \mathbf{p}(a+u)-\mathbf{p}(a)-u\mathbf{p}'(a)-\cdots-\frac{1}{(n-1)!}u^{n-1}\mathbf{p}^{(n-1)}(a)-\frac{1}{n!}u^n\boldsymbol{\lambda},$$

where the constant vector λ is chosen so that $q(h) = 0$. We verify that

$$q(0),\ q'(0),\ q''(0),\ \cdots,\ q^{(n-1)}(0)$$

are all zero.

Now choose an arbitrary vector c and define the scalar $Q(u)$ by

$$Q(u) \equiv c.q(u).$$

It follows that

$$Q(0),\ Q'(0),\ Q''(0),\ \cdots,\ Q^{(n-1)}(0) \text{ and } Q(h)$$

are all zero.

Successive application of *Rolle's theorem* yields

(1) $Q'(h_1) = 0$, where $0 < h_1 < h$ since $Q(0) = 0$ and $Q(h) = 0$,

(2) $Q''(h_2) = 0$, where $0 < h_2 < h_1$ since $Q'(0) = 0$ and $Q'(h_1) = 0$,

$$
\begin{array}{cccccccccccc}
\cdot & & \cdot & & \cdot & & \cdot & & \cdot & & \cdot & \\
& \cdot & & \cdot & & \cdot & & \cdot & & \cdot & & \cdot
\end{array}
$$

(n) $Q^{(n)}(h_n) = 0$, where $0 < h_n < h_{n-1}$ since $Q^{(n-1)}(0) = 0$ and $Q^{(n-1)}(h_{n-1}) = 0$.

Since $0 < h_n < h_{n-1} < \cdots < h_1 < h$, there exists a number θ for which $h_n = \theta h$ and $0 < \theta < 1$. But

$$Q^n(u) = c.q^{(n)}(u) = c.[p^{(n)}(a+u) - \lambda]$$

and so

$$c\,[p^{(n)}(a+\theta h) - \lambda] = 0.$$

However, c is an arbitrary vector and so $\lambda = p^{(n)}(a+\theta h)$. Substitution in $q(h) = 0$ yields equation (22.1) as required.

23 Derivative of a Vector Referred to a Fundamental System

Let the vector $p(u)$ have components $p_i(u)$, $p_j(u)$ and $p_k(u)$ referred to a fundamental system i, j and k. That is,

$$p(u) = p_i(u)i + p_j(u)j + p_k(u)k.$$

Then we have

$$\dot{p}(u) = \frac{d}{du}(p_i i) + \frac{d}{du}(p_j j) + \frac{d}{du}(p_k k).$$

Since i, j and k are constant vectors, we have

$$\dot{p}(u) = \dot{p}_i i + \dot{p}_j j + \dot{p}_k k.$$

EXERCISES

1. Given that $r = a \cos u\,i + a \sin u\,j + bu k$, show that $\dot{r}^2 = a^2 + b^2$,

$$(\dot{r} \times \ddot{r})^2 = a^2(a^2 + b^2) \quad \text{and} \quad [\dot{r}\,\ddot{r}\,\dddot{r}] = a^2 b.$$

2. If $\mathbf{a} = u\mathbf{i} - u^2\mathbf{j} + u^3\mathbf{k}$ and $\mathbf{b} = \sin u\,\mathbf{i} + \cos u\,\mathbf{j}$, calculate (i) $\dfrac{d}{du}\,(\mathbf{a}.\mathbf{b})$,

(ii) $\dfrac{d}{du}\,(\mathbf{a} \times \mathbf{b})$.

24   Partial Derivatives of Vectors

Let $\mathbf{p}(u, v)$ denote a vector function of the independent scalar variables u and v. By this statement we mean that $\mathbf{p}(u, v)$ is uniquely determined when u and v are given values within their ranges.

As an example consider the vector $\mathbf{p} = \mathbf{a} + u\boldsymbol{\alpha} + v\boldsymbol{\beta}$. As u and v vary $\mathbf{p}$ represents the vectors joining the origin to any point of the plane through the point $\mathbf{a}$ in the directions given by $\boldsymbol{\alpha}$ and $\boldsymbol{\beta}$.

The partial derivative $\mathbf{p}_u$ is defined by

$$\mathbf{p}_u = \frac{\partial \mathbf{p}}{\partial u} = \lim_{\Delta u \to 0} \frac{\mathbf{p}(u + \Delta u, v) - \mathbf{p}(u, v)}{\Delta u},$$

provided that this limit exists.

Similarly, the partial derivative $\mathbf{p}_v$ is defined by

$$\mathbf{p}_v = \frac{\partial \mathbf{p}}{\partial v} = \lim_{\Delta v \to 0} \frac{\mathbf{p}(u, v + \Delta v) - \mathbf{p}(u, v)}{\Delta v},$$

provided that this limit exists.

More generally, $\mathbf{p}$ may denote a vector function of any number of independent scalar variables and it is clear how partial derivatives are defined.

We may in the usual way define partial derivatives of higher order. It may be shown, as in real analysis, that under suitable conditions partial differentiation is commutative. For example, we have

$$\frac{\partial}{\partial v}\frac{\partial \mathbf{p}}{\partial u} = \frac{\partial}{\partial u}\frac{\partial \mathbf{p}}{\partial v}.$$

As in the preceding sections we can similarly establish the results that

$$\frac{\partial}{\partial u}\,(\mathbf{p} + \mathbf{q}) = \frac{\partial \mathbf{p}}{\partial u} + \frac{\partial \mathbf{q}}{\partial u},$$

$$\frac{\partial}{\partial u}\,(f\mathbf{a}) = f\frac{\partial \mathbf{a}}{\partial u} + \frac{\partial f}{\partial u}\,\mathbf{a},$$

$$\frac{\partial}{\partial u}(\mathbf{a}.\mathbf{b}) = \mathbf{a}.\frac{\partial \mathbf{b}}{\partial u}+\frac{\partial \mathbf{a}}{\partial u}.\mathbf{b},$$

$$\frac{\partial}{\partial u}(\mathbf{a}\times\mathbf{b}) = \mathbf{a}\times\frac{\partial \mathbf{b}}{\partial u}+\frac{\partial \mathbf{a}}{\partial u}\times\mathbf{b},$$

$$\frac{\partial}{\partial u}\{p_i\mathbf{i}+p_j\mathbf{j}+p_k\mathbf{k}\} = \frac{\partial p_i}{\partial u}\mathbf{i}+\frac{\partial p_j}{\partial u}\mathbf{j}+\frac{\partial p_k}{\partial u}\mathbf{k}.$$

Note carefully that the indices i, j and k refer to the components of a vector with respect to a fundamental system. They will not be used as partial derivative indices.

EXERCISES

1. If $\mathbf{p}=e^{uv}\,\mathbf{i}+(2u-v)\mathbf{j}+v\sin u\,\mathbf{k}$, calculate (i) $\dfrac{\partial \mathbf{p}}{\partial u}$, (ii) $\dfrac{\partial^2 \mathbf{p}}{\partial u^2}$, (iii) $\dfrac{\partial^2 \mathbf{p}}{\partial u\,\partial v}$, (iv) $\dfrac{\partial^2 \mathbf{p}}{\partial v^2}$, (v) $\dfrac{\partial \mathbf{p}}{\partial u}\times\dfrac{\partial \mathbf{p}}{\partial v}$.

2. If $\mathbf{a}=uvw\mathbf{i}+uw^2\mathbf{j}-v^3\mathbf{k}$ and $\mathbf{b}=u^3\mathbf{i}-uvw\mathbf{j}+u^2w\mathbf{k}$, calculate (i) $\dfrac{\partial^2 \mathbf{a}}{\partial u\,\partial v}$ at the origin, (ii) $\dfrac{\partial^2 \mathbf{a}}{\partial v^2}\times\dfrac{\partial^2 \mathbf{b}}{\partial u^2}$ at the point $(1, 1, 0)$.

CHAPTER 4

Applications to Differential Geometry†

25 Curve and Tangent Vector

Consider the vector function $\mathbf{r}(u)$ of the scalar variable u. To each value of u there corresponds a vector whose initial point is at the origin. The other end of the vector determines a point in space. As u varies, this point traces out a curve. To avoid having the curve degenerate to a point, the case when $\mathbf{r}(u)$ is a constant vector is excluded.

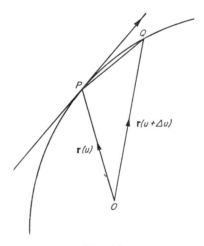

Fig. 22

† Sections 26 and 27 may be omitted by the reader who is not interested in differential geometry. The remaining sections are vital to the subsequent development.

Let P and Q (Fig. 22) correspond to values u and $u+\Delta u$ of the scalar variable. Then $\overrightarrow{OP}$ and $\overrightarrow{OQ}$ are given by the vectors $\mathbf{r}(u)$ and $\mathbf{r}(u+\Delta u)$ respectively.

The **tangent** at a point P on the curve is defined to be the limiting position of the chord PQ as Q tends to coincidence with P. We have

$$\overrightarrow{PQ} = \overrightarrow{OQ} - \overrightarrow{OP} = \mathbf{r}(u+\Delta u) - \mathbf{r}(u)$$

and so

$$\frac{\overrightarrow{PQ}}{\Delta u} = \frac{\mathbf{r}(u+\Delta u) - \mathbf{r}(u)}{\Delta u}.$$

Let Q tend to P. Then Δu tends to zero and we obtain

$$\lim_{\Delta u \to 0} \frac{\overrightarrow{PQ}}{\Delta u} = \dot{\mathbf{r}}(u).$$

But $\lim\limits_{\Delta u \to 0} \dfrac{\overrightarrow{PQ}}{\Delta u}$ is a vector in the direction of the tangent and so the vector $\dot{\mathbf{r}}(u)$ is a **tangent vector** to the curve $\mathbf{r}(u)$ at the point corresponding to the scalar variable u.

The vector $\dot{\mathbf{r}}(u)$ is not *tied* to a fixed point as an initial point and so by the convention introduced in Chapter 2 we ought to represent it by a Greek letter. However, in this and in the following chapters we shall not employ this convention. It is merely necessary to remember that $\mathbf{r}(u)$ is tied to the origin O but other vectors are free in space.

Let the coordinates of the point P given by $\mathbf{r}(u)$ be x, y and z referred to a set of rectangular axes with O as origin. Further, let $\mathbf{i}$, $\mathbf{j}$ and $\mathbf{k}$ denote the fundamental system of vectors with respect to these axes. Then we have

$$\mathbf{r}(u) = x(u)\mathbf{i} + y(u)\mathbf{j} + z(u)\mathbf{k},$$

where $x(u)$, $y(u)$ and $z(u)$ are scalar functions of u.

Introduce the scalar s which measures the distance along the curve from some *fixed* point of the curve. Then we may select s in place of the parameter u to obtain

$$\mathbf{r}(s) = x(s)\mathbf{i} + y(s)\mathbf{j} + z(s)\mathbf{k}.$$

The vector $\mathbf{r}'(s)$, where the prime sign denotes differentiation with respect to s, is now a tangent vector.

From $ds^2 = dx^2 + dy^2 + dz^2$, we have

$$[x'(s)]^2 + [y'(s)]^2 + [z'(s)]^2 = 1.$$

Accordingly

$$\mathbf{r}'(s).\mathbf{r}'(s) = [x'(s)\mathbf{i}+y'(s)\mathbf{j}+z'(s)\mathbf{k}]^2$$
$$= [x'(s)]^2+[y'(s)]^2+[z'(s)]^2$$
$$= 1.$$

That is,

$$\mathbf{T}(s) \equiv \mathbf{r}'(s) = \frac{d\mathbf{r}}{ds}$$

is the *unit* tangent vector to the space curve $\mathbf{r}(s)$ and it clearly points in the direction of increasing s.

Let A and B be points on the curve $\mathbf{r}(u)$ corresponding to the parameter values u_A and u_B. If $\dot{\mathbf{r}}(u)$ is continuous for $u_A \leqslant u \leqslant u_B$, we say that the curve joining AB is a **regular arc**. A **double point** on a curve is a point at which the curve intersects itself or is tangent to itself. Further, a **regular curve** consists of a *finite* number of regular arcs without double points. That is, there can at most be a finite number of points with discontinuous tangents on a regular curve.

26 Frenet Formulae

The vector $\mathbf{T}(s)=\mathbf{r}'(s)$ is the unit tangent vector to the curve $\mathbf{r}(s)$, where s measures arc-distance along the curve from some fixed point on it. Differentiation of $\mathbf{r}'(s).\mathbf{r}'(s)=1$ yields $\mathbf{r}'(s).\mathbf{r}''(s)=0$. That is, the vector $\mathbf{r}''(s)$ is orthogonal to $\mathbf{r}'(s)$. The direction determined by $\mathbf{r}''(s)$ is called the positive direction of the **principal normal**. Let $\mathbf{N}(s)$ denote the unit vector in the positive direction of the principal normal. Accordingly a function κ, positive by convention, called the **curvature** exists such that

$$\mathbf{N}(s) = \frac{1}{\kappa}\mathbf{r}''(s), \qquad (\kappa > 0).$$

This equation can be written in the form

$$\frac{d\mathbf{T}}{ds} = \kappa\mathbf{N}.$$

The unit **binormal** vector $\mathbf{B}(s)$ is defined to be the unit vector orthogonal to both the tangent vector $\mathbf{T}$ and the principal normal vector $\mathbf{N}$ such that $\mathbf{T}$, $\mathbf{N}$ and $\mathbf{B}$ form a right-handed system of unit vectors. Accordingly

$$\mathbf{B} = \mathbf{T}\times\mathbf{N}, \qquad \mathbf{N} = \mathbf{B}\times\mathbf{T}, \qquad \mathbf{T} = \mathbf{N}\times\mathbf{B}.$$

$\mathbf{B}$ is a unit vector and so $\mathbf{B}'$ is orthogonal to $\mathbf{B}$ (see Section 20).

Further we have $\mathbf{B}.\mathbf{T}=0$ and so $\mathbf{B}'.\mathbf{T}+\mathbf{B}.\mathbf{T}'=0$. But $\mathbf{B}.\mathbf{T}'=\mathbf{B}.\kappa\mathbf{N}=0$ and so $\mathbf{B}'.\mathbf{T}=0$. Hence $\mathbf{B}'$ is also orthogonal to $\mathbf{T}$. Accordingly a function $\tau(s)$, called the **torsion**, exists such that

$$\mathbf{B}' = \frac{d\mathbf{B}}{ds} = -\tau\mathbf{N}.$$

It is merely a matter of convention that τ is introduced by this equation with a negative sign. Note carefully that the sign of τ itself cannot be fixed by convention to be positive, but is positive if $\mathbf{B}'$ and $\mathbf{N}$ have opposite directions.

We have
$$\mathbf{N} = \mathbf{B}\times\mathbf{T}$$
and so
$$\begin{aligned}\mathbf{N}' &= \mathbf{B}'\times\mathbf{T}+\mathbf{B}\times\mathbf{T}'\\ &= -\tau\mathbf{N}\times\mathbf{T}+\mathbf{B}\times\kappa\mathbf{N}\\ &= \tau\mathbf{B}-\kappa\mathbf{T}.\end{aligned}$$

The three equations for the derivatives $\mathbf{T}'$, $\mathbf{N}'$ and $\mathbf{B}'$ in terms of the basis formed by $\mathbf{T}$, $\mathbf{N}$ and $\mathbf{B}$ are called the **Frenet formulae**. Collecting the Frenet formulae together, we have

$$\left.\begin{aligned}\mathbf{T}' &= &\kappa\mathbf{N}\\ \mathbf{N}' &= -\kappa\mathbf{T}& &+\tau\mathbf{B}\\ \mathbf{B}' &= &-\tau\mathbf{N}.\end{aligned}\right\}\qquad(26.1)$$

Introduce the **Darboux** vector $\omega=\tau\mathbf{T}+\kappa\mathbf{B}$. Then the Frenet formula can be exhibited in the symmetrical form

$$\mathbf{T}' = \omega\times\mathbf{T},\qquad \mathbf{N}' = \omega\times\mathbf{N},\qquad \mathbf{B}' = \omega\times\mathbf{B}.$$

The three vectors $\mathbf{T}$, $\mathbf{N}$ and $\mathbf{B}$ are called the **trihedral** at a point.

Example 1. Show that the necessary and sufficient condition that a curve be a straight line is that $\kappa=0$.

If the curve is a straight line, the vector $\mathbf{T}$ is constant and so $\mathbf{T}'=\mathbf{0}$. Hence $\kappa=0$.

Conversely, given $\kappa=0$, we have $\mathbf{T}'=\mathbf{0}$ and so $\mathbf{T}$ is a constant vector and the curve is a straight line.

Example 2. The necessary and sufficient condition that a curve lie in a plane is that $\tau=0$.

If the curve lies in a plane, select the origin in this plane. Both $\mathbf{r}'$ and $\mathbf{r}''$ are vectors lying in this plane. Hence $\mathbf{T}$ and $\mathbf{N}$ lie in the plane and so $\mathbf{B}$ is a constant vector, its direction being orthogonal to the plane. Accordingly $\mathbf{B}'=\mathbf{0}$ and this implies that $\tau=0$.

Conversely, given $\tau = 0$ we have $\mathbf{B}' = \mathbf{0}$ and so $\mathbf{B}$ is a constant vector. Let the curve be given by $\mathbf{r}(s)$. Then we have

$$\frac{d}{ds}(\mathbf{r}.\mathbf{B}) = \mathbf{T}.\mathbf{B} + \mathbf{r}.\mathbf{B}' = 0$$

and so $\mathbf{r}.\mathbf{B}$ is a constant. That is, the vectors from the origin to points of the curve are all orthogonal to a fixed direction $\mathbf{B}$. Hence the curve is a plane curve.

27   Curvature and Torsion

We have
$$\mathbf{r}' = \mathbf{T},$$
$$\mathbf{r}'' = \mathbf{T}' = \kappa\mathbf{N},$$
and so
$$\begin{aligned}\mathbf{r}''' &= \kappa'\mathbf{N} + \kappa\mathbf{N}' \\ &= \kappa'\mathbf{N} + \kappa(-\kappa\mathbf{T} + \tau\mathbf{B}) \quad \text{in virtue of (26.1)} \\ &= -\kappa^2\mathbf{T} + \kappa'\mathbf{N} + \kappa\tau\mathbf{B}.\end{aligned}$$
Thus
$$\mathbf{r}''.\mathbf{r}'' = \kappa^2$$
and
$$\mathbf{r}'.\mathbf{r}'' \times \mathbf{r}''' = \mathbf{T}.\kappa\mathbf{N} \times \kappa\tau\mathbf{B} = \kappa^2\tau.$$

Hence we have
$$\kappa = \sqrt{(\mathbf{r}''.\mathbf{r}'')} \quad \text{and} \quad \tau = \frac{\mathbf{r}'.\mathbf{r}'' \times \mathbf{r}'''}{\mathbf{r}''.\mathbf{r}''}. \qquad (27.1)$$

In general the parameter u in $\mathbf{r}(u)$ is not the arc-distance s and so we cannot evaluate κ and τ directly from these equations.

For any vector $\mathbf{a}$ we have

$$\dot{\mathbf{a}} = \frac{d\mathbf{a}}{du} = \frac{d\mathbf{a}}{ds}\frac{ds}{du} = \dot{s}\mathbf{a}'.$$

Using this result in conjunction with the Frenet formulae (26.1) we have
$$\dot{\mathbf{r}} = \dot{s}\,\mathbf{T}, \quad \dot{\mathbf{T}} = \dot{s}\kappa\mathbf{N}, \quad \dot{\mathbf{N}} = \dot{s}(-\kappa\mathbf{T} + \tau\mathbf{B}), \quad \dot{\mathbf{B}} = -\dot{s}\tau\mathbf{N},$$
$$\ddot{\mathbf{r}} = \ddot{s}\,\mathbf{T} + \dot{s}^2\kappa\mathbf{N},$$
$$\dddot{\mathbf{r}} = \dddot{s}\,\mathbf{T} + \dot{s}\ddot{s}\kappa\mathbf{N} + 2\dot{s}\ddot{s}\kappa\mathbf{N} + \dot{s}^2\dot{\kappa}\mathbf{N} + \dot{s}^3\kappa(-\kappa\mathbf{T} + \tau\mathbf{B})$$
and so
$$\dddot{\mathbf{r}} = (\dddot{s} - \dot{s}^3\kappa^2)\mathbf{T} + (3\dot{s}\ddot{s}\kappa + \dot{s}^2\dot{\kappa})\mathbf{N} + \dot{s}^3\kappa\tau\mathbf{B}.$$

Hence

$$\mathbf{r} \times \ddot{\mathbf{r}} = \dot{s}^3 \kappa \mathbf{B},$$
$$|\dot{\mathbf{r}} \times \ddot{\mathbf{r}}| = |\dot{s}^3| \kappa = |\dot{\mathbf{r}}|^3 \kappa,$$
$$\dot{\mathbf{r}}.\ddot{\mathbf{r}} \times \dddot{\mathbf{r}} = \dot{s}^6 \kappa^2 \tau.$$

Thus we obtain

$$\kappa = \frac{|\dot{\mathbf{r}} \times \ddot{\mathbf{r}}|}{|\dot{\mathbf{r}}|^3} \quad \text{and} \quad \tau = \frac{\dot{\mathbf{r}}.\ddot{\mathbf{r}} \times \dddot{\mathbf{r}}}{|\dot{\mathbf{r}} \times \ddot{\mathbf{r}}|^2}. \tag{27.2}$$

Example 1. Calculate the curvature and torsion of the curve

$$\mathbf{r} = a(3u - u^3)\mathbf{i} + 3au^2\mathbf{j} + a(3u + u^3)\mathbf{k}.$$

We have

$$\dot{\mathbf{r}} = 3a(1 - u^2)\mathbf{i} + 6au\mathbf{j} + 3a(1 + u^2)\mathbf{k},$$
$$\ddot{\mathbf{r}} = -6au\mathbf{i} + 6a\mathbf{j} + 6au\mathbf{k},$$
$$\dddot{\mathbf{r}} = -6a\mathbf{i} \qquad\qquad + 6a\mathbf{k},$$

Accordingly, calculation yields

$$|\dot{\mathbf{r}}|^2 = 18a^2(1 + u^2)^2,$$
$$\dot{\mathbf{r}} \times \ddot{\mathbf{r}} = 18a^2(u^2 - 1)\mathbf{i} - 36a^2u\mathbf{j} + 18a^2(u^2 + 1)\mathbf{k},$$
$$|\dot{\mathbf{r}} \times \ddot{\mathbf{r}}|^2 = 2.18^2a^4(1 + u^2)^2,$$
$$\dot{\mathbf{r}}.\ddot{\mathbf{r}} \times \dddot{\mathbf{r}} = \dot{\mathbf{r}} \times \ddot{\mathbf{r}}.\dddot{\mathbf{r}} = 216a^3.$$

Thus we obtain on substitution into equations (27.2) that

$$\kappa = \tau = \frac{1}{3a(1 + u^2)^2}.$$

Example 2. By definition, a **helix** is a space curve whose tangent makes a constant angle with a fixed direction. Show that any single one of the following is a necessary and sufficient condition that a curve be a helix: (i) the principal normal is orthogonal to a fixed direction, (ii) κ/τ is a constant, (iii) $\mathbf{r}'' \times \mathbf{r}'''.\mathbf{r}'''' = 0$.

   (i) By the definition a helix is a curve such that

$$\mathbf{T}.\mathbf{e} = \cos \alpha$$

where $\mathbf{e}$ is a fixed unit vector and α is a constant angle. Differentiation yields $\mathbf{T}'.\mathbf{e} = 0$. Application of the first of the Frenet formulae followed by division by κ yields $\mathbf{N}.\mathbf{e} = 0$. That is, the principal normal is orthogonal to the fixed direction $\mathbf{e}$. Conversely, given $\mathbf{N}.\mathbf{e} = 0$, we have

$$\frac{d}{ds}(\mathbf{T}.\mathbf{e}) = \mathbf{T}'.\mathbf{e} = \kappa\mathbf{N}.\mathbf{e} = 0$$

and so $\mathbf{T}.\mathbf{e}$ is constant as required.

(ii) Differentiation of $\mathbf{N}.\mathbf{e}=0$ yields $(-\kappa\mathbf{T}+\tau\mathbf{B}).\mathbf{e}=0$. Since $\mathbf{N}$ is orthogonal to $\mathbf{e}$, both $\mathbf{T}$ and $\mathbf{B}$ are coplanar with $\mathbf{e}$. Hence $\mathbf{T}.\mathbf{e}=\cos\alpha$ and $\mathbf{B}.\mathbf{e}=\sin\alpha$ if the relative positions are as depicted in Fig. 23. (If

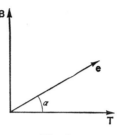

Fig. 23

$\mathbf{B}$ is in the opposite direction, $\mathbf{B}.\mathbf{e}=-\sin\alpha$ and the ensuing calculations require slight modification.) Thus we have $-\kappa\cos\alpha+\tau\sin\alpha=0$ and so $\kappa/\tau=\tan\alpha=$ constant as required.

Conversely, given κ/τ is constant, we can denote the constant by $\tan\alpha$ to give $\kappa\cos\alpha-\tau\sin\alpha=0$. Then we have

$$\frac{d}{ds}(\mathbf{T}\cos\alpha+\mathbf{B}\sin\alpha) = \mathbf{T}'\cos\alpha+\mathbf{B}'\sin\alpha$$

$$= (\kappa\cos\alpha-\tau\sin\alpha)\mathbf{N} = \mathbf{0},$$

and so $\mathbf{T}\cos\alpha+\mathbf{B}\sin\alpha=\mathbf{c}$, where $\mathbf{c}$ is a constant vector. Accordingly $\mathbf{T}.\mathbf{c}=\cos\alpha$ and the curve is a helix.

(iii) We have the relations

$$\mathbf{r}'' = \kappa\mathbf{N},$$
$$\mathbf{r}''' = -\kappa^2\mathbf{T}+\kappa'\mathbf{N}+\kappa\tau\mathbf{B},$$
$$\mathbf{r}'''' = -3\kappa\kappa'\mathbf{T}+(\kappa''-\kappa^3-\kappa\tau^2)\mathbf{N}+(2\kappa'\tau+\kappa\tau')\mathbf{B},$$

and so

$$\mathbf{r}''.\mathbf{r}'''\times\mathbf{r}'''' = \kappa^3(\kappa\tau'-\kappa'\tau) = \kappa^5\frac{d}{ds}\left(\frac{\tau}{\kappa}\right).$$

Thus $\tau/\kappa=$ constant and $\mathbf{r}''.\mathbf{r}'''\times\mathbf{r}''''=0$ each imply the other as required.

EXERCISES

1. For the **circular helix** $\mathbf{r}=a\cos u\,\mathbf{i}+a\sin u\,\mathbf{j}+bu\mathbf{k}$, show that
$$\kappa = a/(a^2+b^2) \quad \text{and} \quad \tau = b/(a^2+b^2).$$

2. For the curve $\mathbf{r}=e^u(\mathbf{i}-\mathbf{j})+\sqrt{2}u\mathbf{k}$, show that
$$\kappa = -\tau = \sqrt{2}/(e^u+e^{-u})^2.$$

3. If a curve lie on a sphere show that $\frac{d}{ds}(\kappa'/\tau\kappa^2)=\tau/\kappa$. (Hint: The equation of the sphere with centre at $\mathbf{c}$ and radius a is $(\mathbf{r}-\mathbf{c}).(\mathbf{r}-\mathbf{c})=a^2$. Successive differentiation yields

$$(\mathbf{r}-\mathbf{c}).\mathbf{T}=0, \quad (\mathbf{r}-\mathbf{c}).\mathbf{N}=-1/\kappa, \quad (\mathbf{r}-\mathbf{c}).\mathbf{B}=\kappa'/\kappa^2\tau$$
$$\text{and} \quad (\mathbf{r}-\mathbf{c}).\mathbf{N}=-\frac{1}{\tau}\frac{d}{ds}\frac{\kappa'}{\kappa^2\tau}.)$$

28   Surfaces and Normals

Consider the vector function $\mathbf{r}(u, v)$ of the two independent scalar variables u and v. To each pair of values of u and v there corresponds a vector whose initial point is at the origin; the other end of the vector determines a point in space. As u and v vary this point traces out a surface. To avoid having the surface degenerate to a curve, the case when $\frac{\partial\mathbf{r}}{\partial u}\times\frac{\partial\mathbf{r}}{\partial v}\equiv 0$ is excluded.

All points on the surface for which v has the constant value v_0 lie on the curve $\mathbf{r}(u, v_0)$ with parameter u. This curve along which u varies is called a u-curve. Similarly all points on the surface for which u has the constant value u_0 lie on the v-curve $\mathbf{r}(u_0, v)$. Collectively, the u-curves and v-curves are called the **parametric curves.**

The vector $\mathbf{r}_u=\partial\mathbf{r}/\partial u$ is a tangent vector to the parametric curve $v=$ constant whilst the vector $\mathbf{r}_v=\partial\mathbf{r}/\partial v$ is a tangent vector to the parametric curve $u=$ constant.

The equations $u=u(t)$, $v=v(t)$ determine the curve $\mathbf{r}(u(t), v(t))$ with parameter t on the surface. It has the tangent vector

$$\frac{d\mathbf{r}}{dt}=\frac{\partial\mathbf{r}}{\partial u}\frac{du}{dt}+\frac{\partial\mathbf{r}}{\partial v}\frac{dv}{dt}=\frac{du}{dt}\mathbf{r}_u+\frac{dv}{dt}\mathbf{r}_v.$$

That is, at a point the tangent vectors to all curves on the surface passing through the point lie in the plane formed by $\mathbf{r}_u$ and $\mathbf{r}_v$. This plane is called the **tangent plane** to the surface at the point.

We define the **normal** at a point on a surface to be the straight line orthogonal to the tangent plane at that point. Let $\mathbf{n}$ denote the unit vector along the normal and be such that the vectors $\mathbf{r}_u$, $\mathbf{r}_v$ and $\mathbf{n}$ form a right-handed system. The vectors $\mathbf{r}_u$ and $\mathbf{r}_v$ are both orthogonal to $\mathbf{n}$ since they lie in the tangent plane. It follows that

$$\mathbf{n}=\frac{\mathbf{r}_u\times\mathbf{r}_v}{|\mathbf{r}_u\times\mathbf{r}_v|}.$$

Example. Obtain the unit normal vector to the sphere

$$\mathbf{r} = a \sin u \cos v \, \mathbf{i} + a \sin u \sin v \, \mathbf{j} + a \cos u \, \mathbf{k}.$$

(This vector equation does represent a sphere of radius a since the components x, y and z of $\mathbf{r}$ satisfy the relation $x^2 + y^2 + z^2 = a^2$. The parameter u represents the colatitude (that is, the complement of the latitude) whilst v measures the longitude. The ranges of the parameters are $0 \leqslant u \leqslant \pi$ and $0 \leqslant v < 2\pi$. The u-curves and v-curves are respectively the meridians and the parallels of latitude.)

We have

$$\mathbf{r}_u = a \cos u \cos v \, \mathbf{i} + a \cos u \sin v \, \mathbf{j} - a \sin u \, \mathbf{k},$$
$$\mathbf{r}_v = -a \sin u \sin v \, \mathbf{i} + a \sin u \cos v \, \mathbf{j},$$

and so

$$\mathbf{r}_u \times \mathbf{r}_v = a^2 \sin^2 u \cos v \, \mathbf{i} + a^2 \sin^2 u \sin v \, \mathbf{j} + a^2 \sin u \cos u \, \mathbf{k},$$
$$|\mathbf{r}_u \times \mathbf{r}_v| = a^2 \sin u,$$

which yields

$$\mathbf{n} = \sin u \cos v \, \mathbf{i} + \sin u \sin v \, \mathbf{j} + \cos u \, \mathbf{k} = \mathbf{r}/a.$$

Thus the positive direction of the unit normal is outwards from the sphere.

EXERCISES

1. Show that $\mathbf{r} = u \cos v \, \mathbf{i} + u \sin v \, \mathbf{j} + f(u)\mathbf{k}$ represents a surface of revolution. What are the parametric curves? Obtain the unit normal vector to the surface.

2. Show that $\mathbf{r} = u \cos v \, \mathbf{i} + u \sin v \, \mathbf{j} + f(v)\mathbf{k}$ represents the **conoid**, which is the surface obtained by revolving a straight line about an axis perpendicular to it whilst simultaneously moving the straight line along the axis. What are the parametric curves? Obtain the unit normal vector to the surface.

29 Length of Arc on a Surface

The distance ds between the two points $\mathbf{r}$ and $\mathbf{r} + d\mathbf{r}$ on the surface $\mathbf{r}(u, v)$ is given by

$$\begin{aligned} ds^2 &= dx^2 + dy^2 + dz^2 \\ &= d\mathbf{r} \cdot d\mathbf{r} \\ &= (\mathbf{r}_u \, du + \mathbf{r}_v \, dv) \cdot (\mathbf{r}_u \, du + \mathbf{r}_v \, dv) \\ &= E \, du^2 + 2F \, du \, dv + G \, dv^2, \end{aligned}$$

where

$$E = \mathbf{r}_u \cdot \mathbf{r}_u, \quad F = \mathbf{r}_u \cdot \mathbf{r}_v, \quad G = \mathbf{r}_v \cdot \mathbf{r}_v.$$

$E\,du^2 + 2F\,du\,dv + G\,dv^2$ is called the **first fundamental form** of the surface $\mathbf{r}(u, v)$.

In particular, the distance d_us along the u-curve for which $dv = 0$ is given by

$$d_us = \sqrt{E}\,du.$$

Similarly, the distance d_vs along the v-curve is given by

$$d_vs = \sqrt{G}\,dv.$$

If every u-curve is orthogonal to every v-curve, we say that the parametric curves form an **orthogonal system**. Hence the necessary condition that the parametric curves form an orthogonal system is that the tangent vectors $\mathbf{r}_u$ and $\mathbf{r}_v$ at each point be orthogonal; that is, if and only if $F = \mathbf{r}_u \cdot \mathbf{r}_v = 0$.

The scalar product $-d\mathbf{r} \cdot d\mathbf{n}$ plays an important role in the differential geometry of surfaces and is called the **second fundamental form**. We have

$$
\begin{aligned}
-d\mathbf{r} \cdot d\mathbf{n} &= -(\mathbf{r}_u\,du + \mathbf{r}_v\,dv) \cdot (\mathbf{n}_u\,du + \mathbf{n}_v\,dv) \\
&= L\,du^2 + 2M\,du\,dv + N\,dv^2,
\end{aligned}
$$

where

$$L = -\mathbf{r}_u \cdot \mathbf{n}_u, \quad 2M = -(\mathbf{r}_u \cdot \mathbf{n}_v + \mathbf{r}_v \cdot \mathbf{n}_u), \quad N = -\mathbf{r}_v \cdot \mathbf{n}_v.$$

Since $\mathbf{n}$ is orthogonal to $\mathbf{r}_u$ and $\mathbf{r}_v$ we have $\mathbf{r}_u \cdot \mathbf{n} = \mathbf{r}_v \cdot \mathbf{n} = 0$. Differentiation yields

$$
\begin{aligned}
\mathbf{r}_u \cdot \mathbf{n}_u + \mathbf{r}_{uu} \cdot \mathbf{n} &= 0, & \mathbf{r}_u \cdot \mathbf{n}_v + \mathbf{r}_{uv} \cdot \mathbf{n} &= 0, \\
\mathbf{r}_v \cdot \mathbf{n}_u + \mathbf{r}_{uv} \cdot \mathbf{n} &= 0, & \mathbf{r}_v \cdot \mathbf{n}_v + \mathbf{r}_{vv} \cdot \mathbf{n} &= 0.
\end{aligned}
$$

It follows that $\mathbf{r}_u \cdot \mathbf{n}_v = \mathbf{r}_v \cdot \mathbf{n}_u = -\mathbf{r}_{uv} \cdot \mathbf{n}$ and so we have

$$
\begin{aligned}
L &= \mathbf{r}_{uu} \cdot \mathbf{n} = [\mathbf{r}_u \mathbf{r}_v \mathbf{r}_{uu}]/|\mathbf{r}_u \times \mathbf{r}_v|, \\
M &= \mathbf{r}_{uv} \cdot \mathbf{n} = [\mathbf{r}_u \mathbf{r}_v \mathbf{r}_{uv}]/|\mathbf{r}_u \times \mathbf{r}_v|, \\
N &= \mathbf{r}_{vv} \cdot \mathbf{n} = [\mathbf{r}_u \mathbf{r}_v \mathbf{r}_{vv}]/|\mathbf{r}_u \times \mathbf{r}_v|.
\end{aligned}
$$

EXERCISES

1. Obtain the first fundamental form of the sphere, surface of revolution and conoid.
2. Show that $|\mathbf{r}_u \times \mathbf{r}_v| = \sqrt{(EG - F^2)}$.
3. Obtain the second fundamental form of the sphere, surface of revolution and conoid.

30   Scalar and Vector Element of Area

Consider (Fig. 24) the four neighbouring points A, B, C, D on the

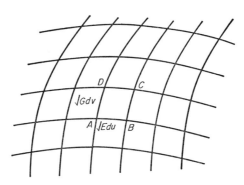

Fig. 24

surface such that the respective values of the parameters at these points are (u, v), $(u+du, v)$, $(u+du, v+dv)$ and $(u, v+dv)$. The distances AB and AD measured along the parametric curves are respectively $d_u s = \sqrt{E}\, du$ and $d_v s = \sqrt{G}\, dv$. The **scalar element of area** dS contained by $ABCD$ is approximately a parallelogram and so $dS = \sin \omega\, d_u s\, d_v s$, where ω is the angle between the tangents to the parametric curves through A. Since $\mathbf{r}_u$ and $\mathbf{r}_v$ are tangent vectors to these parametric curves, we have

$$\sin \omega = \frac{|\mathbf{r}_u \times \mathbf{r}_v|}{|\mathbf{r}_u|\,|\mathbf{r}_v|}.$$

Consequently, we see that

$$dS = |\mathbf{r}_u \times \mathbf{r}_v|\, du\, dv. \tag{30.1}$$

The **vector element of area** $d\mathbf{S}$ is defined by

$$d\mathbf{S} = \mathbf{r}_u \times \mathbf{r}_v\, du\, dv \tag{30.2}$$

and so

$$d\mathbf{S} = \mathbf{n}\, dS. \tag{30.3}$$

CHAPTER 5

Integration

31 Riemann Integral

Let $f(x)$ be a single-valued function of x defined in the interval $a = x_0 \leqslant x \leqslant x_m = b$. Divide this interval into m sub-intervals by the points $x_0, x_1, \ldots, x_m$ where $x_0 < x_1 < x_2 < \cdots < x_{m-1} < x_m$. Let us write $\Delta x_r = x_r - x_{r-1}$, choose ξ_r such that $x_{r-1} \leqslant \xi_r \leqslant x_r$ and form the sum

$$I_m = \sum_{r=1}^{m} f(\xi_r)\, \Delta x_r.$$

Let m tend to infinity in such a way that each Δx_r tends to zero. If the limit of I_m exists and is independent of the mode of subdivision, this limit is called the **Riemann integral** of $f(x)$ from a to b and is denoted by

$$\int_a^b f(x)\, dx.$$

It can be proved that this integral exists when $f(x)$ is continuous in the interval (a, b). However, the integral may exist in cases when the function is not continuous.

32 Line Integral

The vector element of arc length $d\mathbf{s}$ is defined by

$$d\mathbf{s} = \mathbf{T}\, ds,$$

where $\mathbf{T}$ is the unit tangent vector $d\mathbf{r}/ds$ along the curve $\mathbf{r}(s)$. Let Γ denote the portion AB of the regular curve $\mathbf{r}(s)$ corresponding to the range $s_A \leqslant s \leqslant s_B$ of the arc distance s. Consider the vectors $\mathbf{a}(s)$ defined at all points of Γ. Then the **line integral** $\int_\Gamma \mathbf{a} \cdot d\mathbf{s}$ taken over Γ is defined to be the Riemann integral

$$\int_\Gamma \mathbf{a} \cdot d\mathbf{s} = \int_{s_A}^{s_B} \mathbf{a} \cdot \mathbf{T}\, ds.$$

That is, the line integral of a vector is the Riemann integral along the curve of the tangential component of the vector.

Let

$$\mathbf{a} = a_i(x, y, z)\mathbf{i} + a_j(x, y, z)\mathbf{j} + a_k(x, y, z)\mathbf{k}$$

and

$$\mathbf{r} = x(s)\mathbf{i} + y(s)\mathbf{j} + z(s)\mathbf{k}$$

referred to the fundamental system $\mathbf{i}, \mathbf{j}$ and $\mathbf{k}$. Then the line integral is

$$\int_{s_A}^{s_B} \mathbf{a} \cdot \mathbf{T} \, ds = \int_{s_A}^{s_B} \left(\mathbf{a} \cdot \frac{d\mathbf{r}}{ds}\right) ds = \int_{s_A}^{s_B} \left(a_i \frac{dx}{ds} + a_j \frac{dy}{ds} + a_k \frac{dz}{ds}\right) ds$$

$$= \int_{u_A}^{u_B} \left(a_i \frac{dx}{du} + a_j \frac{dy}{du} + a_k \frac{dz}{du}\right) du,$$

where u_A and u_B are the parameter values of u corresponding to A and B.

If Γ is a closed curve it is customary to denote the integral by

$$\oint_\Gamma \mathbf{a} \cdot d\mathbf{s}.$$

Example. Evaluate the line integral of $y\mathbf{i} + z\mathbf{j} + x\mathbf{k}$ over the curves (i) the circle $x^2 + y^2 - 1 = z = 0$, (ii) the triangle in the xy-plane with vertices at $(0, 0)$, $(2, 0)$ and $(2, 1)$, (iii) the skew quadrilateral with vertices at $(0, 0, 0)$, $(1, 0, 0)$, $(1, 1, 0)$ and $(1, 1, 1)$.

The line integral is

$$I = \oint_\Gamma \left(y \frac{dx}{du} + z \frac{dy}{du} + x \frac{dz}{du}\right) du.$$

(i) Over the circle traversed in the counterclockwise direction we have $x = \cos u$, $y = \sin u$, $z = 0$ where $0 \leqslant u \leqslant 2\pi$ and so

$$I = -\int_0^{2\pi} \sin^2 u \, du = -\pi.$$

(ii) Since $z = 0$, we have $I = \oint_\Gamma y \frac{dx}{du} du$. From $(0, 0)$ to $(2, 0)$ we have $y = 0$ and the contribution to the line integral is zero. From $(2, 0)$ to $(2, 1)$ we have $x = 2$ and the contribution is again zero. From $(2, 1)$ to $(0, 0)$ we have $x = -2u$, $y = -u$ for the range $-1 \leqslant u \leqslant 0$ and the contribution is $\int_1^0 2u \, du = -1$. Thus $I = -1$.

(iii) From $(0, 0, 0)$ to $(1, 0, 0)$ we have $y = z = 0$. From $(1, 0, 0)$ to $(1, 1, 0)$ we have $x = 1$, $z = 0$ and so the contributions to the line integral are zero. From $(1, 1, 0)$ to $(1, 1, 1)$ we have $x = y = 1$, $z = u$ for the range $0 \leqslant u \leqslant 1$ and the contribution to the line integral is

$$\int_0^1 du = 1.$$

From $(1, 1, 1)$ to $(0, 0, 0)$ we have $x = y = z = -u$ for the range $-1 \leqslant u \leqslant 0$ and the contribution is $3 \int_{-1}^0 u\, du = -3/2$. Hence the value of I over the skew quadrilateral is $-\frac{1}{2}$.

This example shows that the value of a line integral usually depends on the choice of path.

EXERCISES

1. Calculate the line integral of $yz\mathbf{i} + zx\mathbf{j} + xy\mathbf{k}$ over the curves (i) the straight line joining the points $(b, 0, 0)$ and $(b, 0, 2\pi c)$, (ii) the circular helix $b \cos u\, \mathbf{i} + b \sin u\, \mathbf{j} + cu\mathbf{k}$ which joins the above points.

2. Calculate the line integral of $(y^2 + z^2)\mathbf{i} + (z^2 + x^2)\mathbf{j} + (x^2 + y^2)\mathbf{k}$ from $(0, 0, 0)$ to $(1, 1, 1)$ over the curves (i) the straight line joining the points, (ii) the three straight lines which link these points via the points $(1, 0, 0)$ and $(1, 1, 0)$, (iii) the curve $u\mathbf{i} + u^2\mathbf{j} + u^3\mathbf{k}$.

33 Vector Line Integral

With the notation of the previous section, divide Γ into m sub-intervals by the points with parameters $s_A = s_0, s_1, \ldots, s_m = s_B$. Denote the arc length of the sub-interval (s_{r-1}, s_r) by $\Delta s_r = (s_r - s_{r-1})$ and choose σ_r such that $s_{r-1} \leqslant \sigma_r \leqslant s_r$. Then form the vector sum

$$\mathbf{I}_m = \sum_{r=1}^m \mathbf{a}(\sigma_r)\, \Delta s_r.$$

Let m tend to infinity in such a way that each Δs_r tends to zero. If the limit of $\mathbf{I}_m$ exists and is independent of the mode of subdivision, this limit is called the **vector integral** of $\mathbf{a}$ over the curve Γ and is denoted by

$$\int_\Gamma \mathbf{a}\, ds.$$

Further, the vector line integral $\int_\Gamma \mathbf{a} \times d\mathbf{s}$ is defined by

$$\int_\Gamma \mathbf{a} \times d\mathbf{s} = \int_\Gamma \mathbf{a} \times \mathbf{T}\, ds.$$

Example. Calculate $\oint_{\Gamma} \mathbf{a} \times d\mathbf{s}$, where $\mathbf{a} = \cos u\, \mathbf{i} + \sin u\, \mathbf{j} + e^u\, \mathbf{k}$ and Γ is the circle $\rho \cos u\, \mathbf{i} + \rho \sin u\, \mathbf{j}$. We have $s = \rho u$ and so

$$\mathbf{r} = \rho \cos (s/\rho)\, \mathbf{i} + \rho \sin (s/\rho)\, \mathbf{j}.$$

Hence

$$\mathbf{T} = -\sin (s/\rho)\, \mathbf{i} + \cos (s/\rho)\, \mathbf{j} = -\sin u\, \mathbf{i} + \cos u\, \mathbf{j}$$

and so

$$\mathbf{a} \times \mathbf{T} = -\cos u\, e^u\, \mathbf{i} - \sin u\, e^u\, \mathbf{j} + \mathbf{k}.$$

Accordingly the integral is

$$\rho \int_0^{2\pi} (-\cos u\, e^u\, \mathbf{i} - \sin u\, e^u\, \mathbf{j} + \mathbf{k})\, du = \tfrac{1}{2}\rho\, \{(1 - e^{2\pi})(\mathbf{i} + \mathbf{j}) + 4\pi\mathbf{k}\}.$$

EXERCISES

1. Calculate $\oint_{\Gamma} \mathbf{a}\, ds$ for the vector $\mathbf{a}$ and the curve Γ of the above example.

2. Show that $\oint_{\Gamma} \mathbf{a} \times d\mathbf{s}$, where $\mathbf{a} = z\mathbf{i}$ and Γ is the portion of the circular helix $b \cos u\, \mathbf{i} + b \sin u\, \mathbf{j} + cu\mathbf{k}$ between $(-b, 0, \pi c)$ and $(b, 0, \pi c)$, is

$$\tfrac{1}{2}\pi^2 c^2 \mathbf{j} + 2bc\mathbf{k}.$$

34 Double Integral

Let $f(x, y)$ be a single-valued function of the two independent variables x, y defined over a finite region S of the xy-plane. Divide the region (Fig. 25) into m sub-regions of areas $\Delta S_1, \Delta S_2, \ldots, \Delta S_m$, (this is usually achieved by two families of curves), and choose any

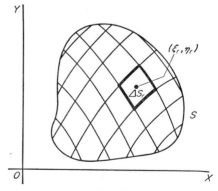

Fig. 25

point (ξ_r, η_r) inside or on the boundary of the sub-region ΔS_r. Then form the sum

$$I_m = \sum_{r=1}^{m} f(\xi_r, \eta_r) \, \Delta S_r.$$

Let m tend to infinity in such a way that each ΔS_r shrinks to a point. If the limit of I_m exists and is independent of the mode of sub-division, this limit is called the **double integral** of $f(x, y)$ over the region S and is denoted by

$$\int_S f(x, y) \, dS.$$

It can be proved that the double integral exists if $f(x, y)$ is con-tinuous over the region S.

The value of a double integral is computed by a suitable choice of sub-regions. For example, if the ΔS_r correspond to the rectangles formed by straight lines parallel to the coordinate axes (Fig. 26) we write $dS = dx \, dy$.

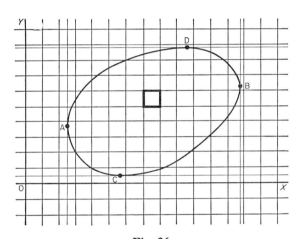

Fig. 26

It can then be shown that

$$\int_S f(x, y) \, dS = \int_a^b \left\{ \int_{y_1(x)}^{y_2(x)} f(x, y) \, dy \right\} dx$$

$$= \int_c^d \left\{ \int_{x_1(y)}^{x_2(y)} f(x, y) \, dx \right\} dy,$$

where $y = y_1(x)$ and $y = y_2(x)$ are the equations of the arcs ACB and

ADB whilst $x = x_1(y)$ and $x = x_2(y)$ are the equations of the arcs *CAD* and *CBD*. Further, *a*, *b* are the abscissae of the points *A*, *B* where the curve has vertical tangents whilst *c*, *d* are the ordinates of the points *C*, *D* where the curve has horizontal tangents.

The regions considered in Figs. 25 and 26 are such that the boundaries are cut in at most two points by parallels to the axes. The definition of double integral can be extended to more complicated regions if they can be dissected into a finite number of sub-regions with the property just mentioned.

Now let the vector $\mathbf{a}(x, y)$ be defined at all points of the region *S*. Then we can form the vector sum

$$\mathbf{I}_m = \sum_{[r=1}^{m} \mathbf{a}(\xi_r, \eta_r) \, \Delta S_r.$$

If the limit of $\mathbf{I}_m$ exists as *m* tends to infinity and is independent of the mode of subdivision, this limit is called the **vector double integral** of $\mathbf{a}(x, y)$ over the region *S* and is denoted by

$$\int_S \mathbf{a}(x, y) \, dS.$$

35 Surface Integral

Let $\mathbf{a}(u, v)$ be a single-valued vector function of *u* and *v* defined over a region *S* of the surface $\mathbf{r}(u, v)$. Divide the region (Fig. 27) into *m* sub-regions of areas $\Delta S_1, \Delta S_2, \ldots, \Delta S_m$ and choose any point

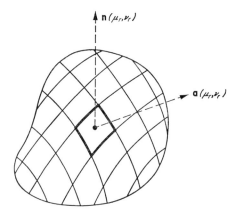

Fig. 27

(μ_r, ν_r) inside or on the boundary of the sub-region ΔS_r. Then form the sum

$$I_m = \sum_{r=1}^{m} \mathbf{a}(\mu_r, \nu_r) \cdot \mathbf{n}(\mu_r, \nu_r) \, \Delta S_r$$

where $\mathbf{n}$ is the unit normal vector. Let m tend to infinity in such a way that each ΔS_r shrinks to a point. If the limit of I_m exists and is independent of the mode of subdivision, it is called the **surface integral** of $\mathbf{a}(u, v)$ over the region S of the surface $\mathbf{r}(u, v)$ and is denoted by

$$\int_S \mathbf{a} \cdot \mathbf{n} \, dS = \int_S \mathbf{a} \cdot d\mathbf{S},$$

where $d\mathbf{S} = \mathbf{n} \, dS$.

The surface integral can be evaluated as a double integral by interpreting u, v as rectangular Cartesian coordinates on a suitable region $\bar{S}$ of the uv-plane. In addition (see equation (30.1)) we replace dS by $|\mathbf{r}_u \times \mathbf{r}_v| \, du \, dv$. Accordingly,

$$\int_S \mathbf{a} \cdot d\mathbf{S} = \int_{\bar{S}} \mathbf{a} \cdot \mathbf{n} |\mathbf{r}_u \times \mathbf{r}_v| \, d\bar{S}, \qquad (d\bar{S} = du \, dv).$$

In particular, the area of any region S of the surface is given by

$$\int_S dS = \int_S \mathbf{n} \cdot d\mathbf{S} = \int_{\bar{S}} |\mathbf{r}_u \times \mathbf{r}_v| \, d\bar{S}.$$

From $\left| \sum_{r=1}^{m} \alpha_r \right| \leqslant \sum_{r=1}^{m} |\alpha_r|$ and $|\mathbf{a} \cdot \mathbf{n}| \leqslant |\mathbf{a}|$ it follows from the surface integral definition that

$$\left| \int_S \mathbf{a} \cdot d\mathbf{S} \right| \leqslant \int_S |\mathbf{a} \cdot \mathbf{n}| \, dS \leqslant \int_S |\mathbf{a}| \, dS. \qquad (35.1)$$

A surface which encloses a finite volume will be called a closed surface. For example, a sphere is a closed surface but a hemisphere without its diametral plane is not a closed surface. For closed surfaces it is conventional to arrange that the positive direction of the normal is outwards from the surface. If S is a closed surface it is customary to denote the surface integral by $\oint_S \mathbf{a} \cdot d\mathbf{S}$.

Three types of **vector surface integrals** are defined in terms of the corresponding vector double integrals by

$$\int_S \mathbf{a}\, dS = \int_{\bar{S}} \mathbf{a}\, |\mathbf{r}_u \times \mathbf{r}_v|\, d\bar{S},$$

$$\int_S \mathbf{a} \times d\mathbf{S} = \int_{\bar{S}} \mathbf{a} \times \mathbf{n}\, |\mathbf{r}_u \times \mathbf{r}_v|\, d\bar{S},$$

and

$$\int_S f\, d\mathbf{S} = \int_{\bar{S}} f\mathbf{n}\, |\mathbf{r}_u \times \mathbf{r}_v|\, d\bar{S},$$

where $f(u, v)$ is a scalar function defined over S.

Example. Evaluate $\int_S \mathbf{a}\, dS$, $\int_S \mathbf{a}.d\mathbf{S}$ and $\int_S \mathbf{a} \times d\mathbf{S}$ for the vector $\mathbf{a} = \cos u \cos v\, \mathbf{i} + \cos u \sin v\, \mathbf{j} - \sin u\, \mathbf{k}$ over the octant of the sphere $\mathbf{r} = \rho \sin u \cos v\, \mathbf{i} + \rho \sin u \sin v\, \mathbf{j} + \rho \cos u\, \mathbf{k}$ corresponding to $0 \leqslant u \leqslant \pi/2$ and $0 \leqslant v \leqslant \pi/2$.

We can readily calculate that

$$|\mathbf{r}_u \times \mathbf{r}_v| = \rho^2 \sin u,$$

$$\mathbf{n} = \sin u \cos v\, \mathbf{i} + \sin u \sin v\, \mathbf{j} + \cos u\, \mathbf{k},$$

$$\mathbf{a}.\mathbf{n} = 0 \quad \text{and} \quad \mathbf{a} \times \mathbf{n} = \sin v\, \mathbf{i} - \cos v\, \mathbf{j}.$$

Hence we have $\int \mathbf{a}.d\mathbf{S} = 0$ and

$$\int_S \mathbf{a}\, dS = \rho^2 \int_{\bar{S}} (\cos u \cos v\, \mathbf{i} + \cos u \sin v\, \mathbf{j} - \sin u\, \mathbf{k}) \sin u\, d\bar{S},$$

$$\int_S \mathbf{a} \times d\mathbf{S} = \rho^2 \int_{\bar{S}} (\sin v\, \mathbf{i} - \cos v\, \mathbf{j}) \sin u\, d\bar{S},$$

where $\bar{S}$ is the rectangle corresponding to $0 \leqslant u \leqslant \pi/2$ and $0 \leqslant v \leqslant \pi/2$ in the uv-plane.

Simple calculations with $d\bar{S} = du\, dv$ now yield

$$\int_S \mathbf{a}\, dS = \tfrac{1}{2}\rho^2\, (\mathbf{i} + \mathbf{j} - \tfrac{1}{4}\pi^2 \mathbf{k})$$

and

$$\int_S \mathbf{a} \times d\mathbf{S} = \rho^2\, (\mathbf{i} - \mathbf{j}).$$

EXERCISES

1. Evaluate $\int_S \mathbf{a} \, dS$, $\int_S \mathbf{a}.d\mathbf{S}$ and $\int_S \mathbf{a} \times d\mathbf{S}$ for the vector

$$\mathbf{a} = (y+z)\mathbf{i}+(z+x)\mathbf{j}+(x+y)\mathbf{k},$$

where S is the surface of the cube bounded by $x=0, y=0, z=0, x=1, y=1$ and $z=1$.

2. Evaluate $\int_S xyz \, dS$ over an octant of a unit sphere whose centre is at the origin.

36 Volume Integral

Let $f(x, y, z)$ be a single-valued function of x, y and z defined throughout a three-dimensional region V. Divide V into m sub-regions of volumes $\varDelta V_1, \varDelta V_2, \ldots, \varDelta V_m$. Choose any point (ξ_r, η_r, ζ_r) inside or on the boundary of the region $\varDelta V_r$. Then form the sum

$$I_m = \sum_{r=1}^{m} f(\xi_r, \eta_r, \zeta_r) \varDelta V_r.$$

If the limit of I_m exists as m tends to infinity in such a way that each $\varDelta V_r$ shrinks to a point and if the limit is independent of the mode of subdivision, the limit is called the **volume integral** of $f(x, y, z)$ over the region V and is denoted by

$$\int_V f(x, y, z) \, dV.$$

If the subdivision is made by planes parallel to the coordinate planes, the volume integral can be evaluated as an iterated integral by a generalization of the method outlined in Section 34.

Corresponding to the vector function $\mathbf{a}(x, y, z)$, defined in the region V, we can form the vector sum

$$\mathbf{I}_m = \sum_{r=1}^{m} \mathbf{a}(\xi_r, \eta_r, \zeta_r) \varDelta V_r$$

and so in the usual way by a limiting process obtain the **vector volume integral**

$$\int_V \mathbf{a} \, dV.$$

EXERCISE

1. Evaluate $\int_V \mathbf{a} \, dV$ for the vector $x\mathbf{i}+y\mathbf{j}+z\mathbf{k}$, where V is the region bounded by the surfaces $x=0, y=0, y=6, z=4$ and $z=x^2$.

5—V.A.

CHAPTER 6

Gradient of a Scalar Function

37 Directional Derivative

In this and the following chapters the function $f(\mathbf{r}) \equiv f(x, y, z)$ will denote a single-valued function of the rectangular Cartesian co-ordinates x, y and z defined at all points of a region of space. We sometimes say that a **scalar field** f has been defined in a region.

We define the **directional derivative** $D_\alpha f(\mathbf{r})$ of $f(\mathbf{r})$ in the direction given by the vector $\boldsymbol{\alpha}$ by

$$D_\alpha f(\mathbf{r}) = \lim_{h \to 0} \frac{f(\mathbf{r} + h\boldsymbol{\alpha}) - f(\mathbf{r})}{h}$$

provided that this limit exists.

Let P and Q be the neighbouring points (x, y, z) and $(x + \Delta x, y + \Delta y, z + \Delta z)$ at a distance Δs apart. We use the notation $\dfrac{\partial f}{\partial s}$ for the directional derivative of $f(\mathbf{r})$ along the direction $\overrightarrow{PQ}$. In this case $h = \Delta s$ and $\boldsymbol{\alpha} = \Delta x \mathbf{i} + \Delta y \mathbf{j} + \Delta z \mathbf{k}$ and so

$$\frac{\partial f}{\partial s} = \lim_{\Delta s \to 0} \frac{\Delta f}{\Delta s} = \lim_{\Delta s \to 0} \frac{f(x + \Delta x, y + \Delta y, z + \Delta z) - f(x, y, z)}{\Delta s} \quad . \quad (37.1)$$

We have

$$\Delta f = \left(\frac{\partial f}{\partial x} + \varepsilon_1\right) \Delta x + \left(\frac{\partial f}{\partial y} + \varepsilon_2\right) \Delta y + \left(\frac{\partial f}{\partial z} + \varepsilon_3\right) \Delta z,$$

where ε_1, ε_2 and ε_3 tend to zero as Δx, Δy and Δz tend to zero. Divide by Δs and proceed to the limit as Δs tends to zero with the result that

$$\frac{\partial f}{\partial s} = \frac{\partial f}{\partial x}\frac{dx}{ds} + \frac{\partial f}{\partial y}\frac{dy}{ds} + \frac{\partial f}{\partial z}\frac{dz}{ds}. \qquad (37.2)$$

It is clear from the definition of directional derivative that the partial derivatives $\frac{\partial f}{\partial x}, \frac{\partial f}{\partial y}$ and $\frac{\partial f}{\partial z}$ are the directional derivatives in the directions of the coordinate axes.

Simple calculations yield

$$\frac{\partial}{\partial s}(af+bg) = a\frac{\partial f}{\partial s} + b\frac{\partial g}{\partial s},$$

$$\frac{\partial}{\partial s}(fg) = f\frac{\partial g}{\partial s} + g\frac{\partial f}{\partial s}$$

where a and b are constants.

The differential df is defined by

$$df = \frac{\partial f}{\partial x}dx + \frac{\partial f}{\partial y}dy + \frac{\partial f}{\partial z}dz$$

and so

$$df = \frac{\partial f}{\partial s}ds.$$

EXERCISE

1. If $f = x^3 + y^3 + z^3$, find the directional derivative of f at the point $(1, -1, 2)$ in the direction of (i) the vector $\mathbf{i}+2\mathbf{j}+\mathbf{k}$, (ii) the vector $\mathbf{j}-\mathbf{k}$, (iii) in the direction of the normal to the surface $x^3 + y^3 + z^3 = 8$.

2. Find the directional derivative of $|\mathbf{A}|^2$ in the direction $\boldsymbol{\alpha}$.

38   Gradient of a Scalar Function

The equation $f(x, y, z) = k$ represents a surface. If we vary the value of k we obtain a family of surfaces, one of which passes through any particular point. Let $\mathbf{n}$ be the unit normal vector to the surface. The directional derivative of $f(x, y, z)$ in the direction of the normal to the surface is called the **normal derivative** and denoted by $\partial f/\partial n$. We define the **gradient** of $f(x, y, z)$, denoted by grad f, to be the vector

$$\operatorname{grad} f = \frac{\partial f}{\partial n}\mathbf{n}. \qquad (38.1)$$

Note carefully that this definition is invariant in the sense that grad f is independent of the choice of the basis.

It follows from the definition that grad $c = 0$ if c is a constant. Let PN of length Δn be drawn (Fig. 28) along the normal to

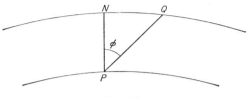

Fig. 28

$f(x, y, z) =$ constant at P and PQ of length Δs be drawn along a direction making an angle φ with PN such that N and Q are both on the same neighbouring surface of the family. Accordingly, NQ is approximately orthogonal to NP and so we have $\Delta n \approx \Delta s \cos \varphi$.

From the definition (37.1) we have that the directional derivative $\partial f/\partial s$ along PQ is given by

$$\frac{\partial f}{\partial s} = \frac{\partial f}{\partial n} \cos \varphi.$$

Hence the maximum value of the directional derivative is attained in the direction of the normal.

Let $\mathbf{T}$ denote the unit vector in the direction $\overrightarrow{PQ}$. Then

$$\cos \varphi = \mathbf{T} . \mathbf{n}$$

and so

$$\frac{\partial f}{\partial s} = \frac{\partial f}{\partial n} \mathbf{T} . \mathbf{n} = \frac{\partial f}{\partial n} \mathbf{n} . \mathbf{T} = \operatorname{grad} f . \mathbf{T}.$$

That is, the directional derivative in any direction is the component in that direction of the gradient.

Further, we have

$$df = \frac{\partial f}{\partial s} ds = \operatorname{grad} f . \mathbf{T} \, ds = \operatorname{grad} f . d\mathbf{s},$$

where $d\mathbf{s} = \mathbf{T} \, ds$.

Let $\dfrac{\partial f}{\partial s_1}, \dfrac{\partial f}{\partial s_2}$ and $\dfrac{\partial f}{\partial s_3}$ be the directional derivatives in the directions of the three mutually orthogonal unit vectors $\mathbf{e}_1$, $\mathbf{e}_2$ and $\mathbf{e}_3$. Then

$$\operatorname{grad} f . \mathbf{e}_1 = \frac{\partial f}{\partial s_1}, \quad \operatorname{grad} f . \mathbf{e}_2 = \frac{\partial f}{\partial s_2}, \quad \operatorname{grad} f . \mathbf{e}_3 = \frac{\partial f}{\partial s_3},$$

since we have just seen that the directional derivative is the component of the gradient. Hence

$$\operatorname{grad} f = \frac{\partial f}{\partial s_1}\,\mathbf{e}_1 + \frac{\partial f}{\partial s_2}\,\mathbf{e}_2 + \frac{\partial f}{\partial s_3}\,\mathbf{e}_3.$$

In particular, if we identify $\mathbf{e}_1$, $\mathbf{e}_2$ and $\mathbf{e}_3$ with the fundamental system $\mathbf{i}$, $\mathbf{j}$ and $\mathbf{k}$, the corresponding directional derivatives are the partial derivatives $\frac{\partial f}{\partial x}$, $\frac{\partial f}{\partial y}$ and $\frac{\partial f}{\partial z}$. Accordingly, we have

$$\operatorname{grad} f = \frac{\partial f}{\partial x}\,\mathbf{i} + \frac{\partial f}{\partial y}\,\mathbf{j} + \frac{\partial f}{\partial z}\,\mathbf{k}.$$

From the relation $\frac{\partial f}{\partial s} = \operatorname{grad} f.\mathbf{T}$ and the properties of directional derivatives it follows that

$$\operatorname{grad}(af+bg).\mathbf{T} = \frac{\partial}{\partial s}(af+bg)$$
$$= a\frac{\partial f}{\partial s} + b\frac{\partial g}{\partial s}$$
$$= a\operatorname{grad} f.\mathbf{T} + b\operatorname{grad} g.\mathbf{T}$$
$$= (a\operatorname{grad} f + b\operatorname{grad} g).\mathbf{T},$$

where a and b are constants.

Further, we have

$$\operatorname{grad}(fg).\mathbf{T} = \frac{\partial}{\partial s}(fg)$$
$$= f\frac{\partial g}{\partial s} + g\frac{\partial f}{\partial s}$$
$$= f\operatorname{grad} g.\mathbf{T} + g\operatorname{grad} f.\mathbf{T}$$
$$= (f\operatorname{grad} g + g\operatorname{grad} f).\mathbf{T}.$$

Since $\mathbf{T}$ is an arbitrary unit vector, we have

$$\operatorname{grad}(af+bg) = a\operatorname{grad} f + b\operatorname{grad} g,$$
$$\operatorname{grad}(fg) = f\operatorname{grad} g + g\operatorname{grad} f.$$

EXERCISES

1. Calculate the normal derivatives at $(-1, 1, 1)$ of the functions (i) $yz+zx+xy$, (ii) xyz, (iii) x^3-y^2+z.

2.† Show that $\operatorname{grad} r = \mathbf{r}/r$ and $\operatorname{grad} r^n = n r^{n-2} \mathbf{r}$. (Hint: Use a fundamental system of basis vectors.)

3. Show that $\operatorname{grad}(f/g) = (g \operatorname{grad} f - f \operatorname{grad} g)/g^2$.

4. If $\mathbf{c}$ is a constant vector, show that
   (i) $\operatorname{grad} \mathbf{c} \cdot \mathbf{r} = \mathbf{c}$,
   (ii) $\operatorname{grad} |\mathbf{c} \times \mathbf{r}|^n = n |\mathbf{c} \times \mathbf{r}|^{n-2} \mathbf{c} \times (\mathbf{r} \times \mathbf{c})$,
   (iii) $\mathbf{c} \cdot \operatorname{grad} \left(\mathbf{c} \cdot \operatorname{grad} \dfrac{1}{r} \right) = \{3(\mathbf{c} \cdot \mathbf{r})^2 - \mathbf{c}^2 \mathbf{r}^2\}/r^5$.

5. Show that $\operatorname{grad} f(r) = f'(r) \mathbf{r}/r$.

39 Irrotational Vector

If a vector $\mathbf{a}(x, y, z)$ is defined at all points of a region, we say that $\mathbf{a}$ is a **vector field** in the region.

The **circulation** of the vector field $\mathbf{a}$ round a closed circuit Γ is defined to be the value of the line integral $\oint_{\Gamma} \mathbf{a} \cdot d\mathbf{s}$. The vector field $\mathbf{a}$ is said to be **irrotational** if its circulation round all circuits is zero.

A region R is said to be **connected** if any two points of the region can be joined by an arc lying completely in the region. Figures 29(a) and (b) depict connected regions, but the region in Fig. 29(c) is not connected.

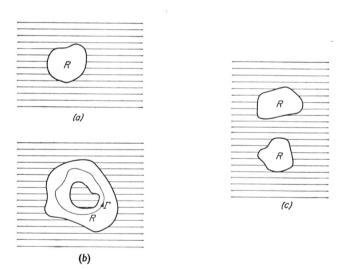

(a)

(b)

(c)

Fig. 29

† The vector $\mathbf{r}$ in this text will always denote the position vector relative to some origin.

A region is said to be **simply-connected** if every closed curve in the region can be shrunk continuously to a point in the region. The region R of Fig. 29(a) is simply-connected, whilst that of Fig. 29(b) is not simply-connected as the curve Γ cannot be shrunk continuously to a point without leaving the region.

A necessary and sufficient condition that the continuous vector field $\mathbf{a}$ be irrotational in a connected region is that a single-valued function $f(x, y, z)$ exists for which $\mathbf{a} = \operatorname{grad} f$.

To prove the sufficiency, we note that

$$\oint_\Gamma \mathbf{a}.d\mathbf{s} = \oint_\Gamma \operatorname{grad} f.d\mathbf{s} = \oint_\Gamma df = [f]_\Gamma = 0$$

since f is single-valued.

To prove the necessity, let $\oint_\Gamma \mathbf{a}.d\mathbf{s} = 0$ and consider the case when the circuit Γ is the curve $LMPNL$ in Fig. 30. The line integral round this closed circuit is zero and so we have

$$\int_{LMP} \mathbf{a}.d\mathbf{s} = \int_{LNP} \mathbf{a}.d\mathbf{s}.$$

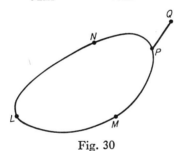

Fig. 30

Choose L to be a *fixed* point. It follows that $\int \mathbf{a}.d\mathbf{s}$ taken along any path from L to P inside the region is a function of the position P and so we may write

$$f(P) = \int_{LP} \mathbf{a}.d\mathbf{s}.$$

The value of this function at a neighbouring point Q is given by

$$f(Q) = \int_{LP} \mathbf{a}.d\mathbf{s} + \int_{PQ} \mathbf{a}.d\mathbf{s}.$$

Hence the change Δf in f from P to Q is

$$\Delta f = f(Q) - f(P) = \int_{PQ} \mathbf{a}.d\mathbf{s}.$$

Select the straight line path from P to Q. By continuity, we have that along PQ

$$\mathbf{a} = \mathbf{a}(P) + \mathbf{\varepsilon}$$

where $\mathbf{\varepsilon}$ tends to zero as Q tends to P. Accordingly

$$\Delta f = \mathbf{a}(P).d\mathbf{s} + \int_{PQ} \mathbf{\varepsilon}.d\mathbf{s}.$$

The integral term is of higher order than ds and so in the limit we have

$$df = \mathbf{a}.d\mathbf{s}.$$

But $df = \operatorname{grad} f.d\mathbf{s}$. Thus

$$(\mathbf{a} - \operatorname{grad} f).d\mathbf{s} = 0.$$

This equation is true for arbitrary $d\mathbf{s}$ and so we have the required result that

$$\mathbf{a} = \operatorname{grad} f.$$

Example. Obtain the conditions that the vector

$$x^a y^b z^c (x^l \mathbf{i} + y^m \mathbf{j} + z^n \mathbf{k})$$

be irrotational.

By the theorem just proved there must be a scalar function $f(x, y, z)$ such that

$$\frac{\partial f}{\partial x} = x^{a+l} y^b z^c, \quad \frac{\partial f}{\partial y} = x^a y^{b+m} z^c, \quad \frac{\partial f}{\partial z} = x^a y^b z^{c+n}.$$

Integration yields the following three possibilities for f:

$$\frac{x^{a+l+1} y^b z^c}{a+l+1} + \psi_1(y, z),$$

$$\frac{x^a y^{b+m+1} z^c}{b+m+1} + \psi_2(z, x),$$

$$\frac{x^a y^b z^{c+n+1}}{c+n+1} + \psi_3(x, y),$$

where ψ_1, ψ_2, ψ_3 are suitably chosen functions of the variables indicated. The three values for f can be reconciled if

(i) $l = m = n = -1$, $a = b = c$. The corresponding scalar function is $f = (xyz)^a/a$,

(ii) $a = b = c = 0$ and the corresponding scalar function is

$$f = \frac{x^{l+1}}{l+1} + \frac{y^{m+1}}{m+1} + \frac{z^{n+1}}{n+1}.$$

EXERCISES

1. Show that (i) $\oint_\Gamma \mathbf{r}\,.\,d\mathbf{s}=0$, (ii) $\oint_\Gamma \mathbf{c}\,.\,d\mathbf{s}=0$ for any constant vector $\mathbf{c}$.

2. It is given that P, Q and R are functions of x, y and z with continuous partial derivatives of the first order inside a simply-connected region which contains the path Γ joining (x_0, y_0, z_0) to (x, y, z) by the straight lines connecting the points via (x, y_0, z_0) and (x, y, z_0). Show that

$$\mathbf{a} = P\mathbf{i}+Q\mathbf{j}+R\mathbf{k}$$

is irrotational if and only if

$$\frac{\partial R}{\partial y} = \frac{\partial Q}{\partial z}, \quad \frac{\partial P}{\partial z} = \frac{\partial R}{\partial x} \quad \text{and} \quad \frac{\partial Q}{\partial x} = \frac{\partial P}{\partial y}.$$

(Hint: define $A(x, y, z) = \displaystyle\int_\Gamma \mathbf{a}\,.\,d\mathbf{s}$ and show that $\mathbf{a}=\text{grad } A$.)

3. Determine which, if any, of the following vector fields are irrotational:
(i) $(\boldsymbol{\lambda}.\mathbf{r})\boldsymbol{\mu}$, (ii) $(\boldsymbol{\lambda}.\boldsymbol{\mu})\mathbf{r}$, (iii) $(\boldsymbol{\lambda}.\mathbf{r})\boldsymbol{\mu}+(\boldsymbol{\mu}.\mathbf{r})\boldsymbol{\lambda}$, (iv) $(\boldsymbol{\lambda}.\mathbf{r})\boldsymbol{\mu}-(\boldsymbol{\mu}.\mathbf{r})\boldsymbol{\lambda}$, where $\boldsymbol{\lambda}$ and $\boldsymbol{\mu}$ are constant vectors such that $\boldsymbol{\lambda}\times\boldsymbol{\mu}\neq\mathbf{0}$. In appropriate cases, obtain the scalar field whose gradient is the irrotational field of vectors.

40 Integral Definition of Gradient

Let S be a *closed* surface which contains a volume V and define the vector $\mathbf{a}$ from the scalar field $f(x, y, z)$ by the equation

$$\mathbf{a} = \lim_{V\to 0} \frac{\oint_S f\,d\mathbf{S}}{V}$$

provided that the limit exists.

Choose S to be a cylinder (Fig. 31) with its generators parallel to the fixed unit vector $\mathbf{c}$. Then

$$\mathbf{a}.\mathbf{c} = \lim_{V\to 0} \frac{1}{V}\oint_S f\mathbf{c}\,.\,d\mathbf{S}.$$

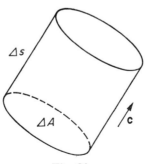

Fig. 31

On the curved surface of the cylinder $\mathbf{c}$ is orthogonal to the unit normal vector $\mathbf{n}$ and so $\mathbf{c}.d\mathbf{S} = \mathbf{c}.\mathbf{n}\, dS = 0$. Thus the total contribution to the surface integral comes from the base and top of the cylinder.

Let the cylinder be of height Δs and cross-sectional area ΔA. On the base $\mathbf{c}.d\mathbf{S} = \mathbf{c}.(-\mathbf{c}\, dS) = -dS$ whilst on the top

$$\mathbf{c}.d\mathbf{S} = \mathbf{c}.\mathbf{c}\, dS = dS.$$

By the mean-value theorems, the contributions of $\oint_S f\mathbf{c}.d\mathbf{S}$ to the base and top are

$$-(f+\varepsilon_1)\,\Delta A \quad \text{and} \quad \left(f+\frac{\partial f}{\partial s}\Delta s+\varepsilon_2\right)\Delta A,$$

where ε_1 and ε_2 tend to zero as ΔA tends to zero. Thus

$$\mathbf{a}.\mathbf{c} = \lim_{\substack{\Delta s\to 0 \\ \Delta A\to 0}} \frac{\left(\frac{\partial f}{\partial s}\Delta s+\varepsilon_2-\varepsilon_1\right)\Delta A}{\Delta s\,\Delta A} = \frac{\partial f}{\partial s}.$$

But the component of $\operatorname{grad} f$ in the direction $\mathbf{c}$ is $\dfrac{\partial f}{\partial s}$ and so

$$\mathbf{a} = \operatorname{grad} f.$$

That is, $\operatorname{grad} f$ can be defined as the limit of an integral. Since the unit vector $\mathbf{c}$ is arbitrary, it follows from this definition that $\operatorname{grad} f$ is independent of the choice of the basis vectors.

CHAPTER 7

Divergence of a Vector

41 Divergence of a Vector

Let **a** be a vector field defined inside a closed surface S which encloses a volume V. We define a scalar field associated with **a**, called the **divergence** of the vector **a** and written div **a**, by the relation

$$\text{div } \mathbf{a} = \lim_{V \to 0} \frac{\oint_S \mathbf{a} . d\mathbf{S}}{V} \qquad (41.1)$$

provided that the limit exists. It is clear from the definition that div **a** is independent of the choice of the basis vectors.

If λ, μ and **c** are constants, we have from the definition that

$$\text{div } (\lambda \mathbf{a} + \mu \mathbf{b}) = \lambda \text{ div } \mathbf{a} + \mu \text{ div } \mathbf{b}$$

and

$$\text{div } (f\mathbf{c}) = \lim_{V \to 0} \left\{ \frac{1}{V} \oint_S f\mathbf{c} . d\mathbf{S} \right\} = \mathbf{c} . \lim_{V \to 0} \left\{ \frac{1}{V} \oint_S f \, d\mathbf{S} \right\}.$$

That is,

$$\text{div } (f\mathbf{c}) = \mathbf{c} . \text{grad} f.$$

Substitute $f = 1$ and we obtain div $\mathbf{c} = 0$.

Let $\mathbf{a} = a_i \mathbf{i} + a_j \mathbf{j} + a_k \mathbf{k}$ with respect to the fundamental system **i, j, k**. Then we have

$$\text{div } \mathbf{a} = \text{div } (a_i \mathbf{i}) + \text{div } (a_j \mathbf{j}) + \text{div } (a_k \mathbf{k})$$
$$= \mathbf{i} . \text{grad } a_i + \mathbf{j} . \text{grad } a_j + \mathbf{k} . \text{grad } a_k.$$

But $\mathbf{i} . \text{grad } a_i$ is the directional derivative along the x-axis, etc. Thus

$$\text{div } \mathbf{a} = \frac{\partial a_i}{\partial x} + \frac{\partial a_j}{\partial y} + \frac{\partial a_k}{\partial z}.$$

65

The Laplacian† Δf is defined by

$$\Delta f = \operatorname{div} \operatorname{grad} f$$

and so in a Cartesian coordinate system we have

$$\Delta f = \frac{\partial^2 f}{\partial x^2} + \frac{\partial^2 f}{\partial y^2} + \frac{\partial^2 f}{\partial z^2}.$$

EXERCISES

1. Show that $\operatorname{div} r^n \mathbf{r} = (n+3)r^n$.
2. If $\mathbf{c}$ is a constant vector, show that (i) $\operatorname{div}(\mathbf{c} \times \mathbf{r}) = 0$, (ii) $\operatorname{div}(\mathbf{c} \cdot \mathbf{r}\mathbf{c}) = \mathbf{c}^2$, (iii) $\operatorname{div}\{\mathbf{c} \times (\mathbf{r} \times \mathbf{c})\} = 2\mathbf{c}^2$.
3. If $\mathbf{p} = x^2\mathbf{i} + y^2\mathbf{j} + z^2\mathbf{k}$, $\mathbf{q} = yz\mathbf{i} + zx\mathbf{j} + xy\mathbf{k}$ and $\mathbf{u} = xyz\mathbf{j}$, calculate (i) $\operatorname{div} \mathbf{p}$, (ii) $\operatorname{div} \mathbf{q}$, (iii) $\operatorname{div} \mathbf{u}$, (iv) $\operatorname{div}(\mathbf{q} \times \mathbf{u})$, (v) $\operatorname{grad}(\mathbf{p} \cdot \mathbf{q})$, (vi) $\operatorname{grad} \operatorname{div}(\mathbf{q} \times \mathbf{p})$, (vii) $\Delta[\mathbf{pqu}]$.
4. Calculate (i) $\Delta(1/r)$, (ii) Δr^2, (iii) $\Delta f(r)$, (iv) $\Delta[\operatorname{div}(\mathbf{r}/r^2)]$.

42 Gauss's Theorem

Consider a finite closed surface S enclosing a volume V. Divide V into m sub-regions of volumes $\Delta V_1, \Delta V_2, \ldots, \Delta V_m$ and choose any point (ξ_r, η_r, ζ_r) inside or on the boundary ΔS_r of the sub-region ΔV_r. From the divergence definition we have

$$\Delta V_r \operatorname{div} \mathbf{a}(\xi_r, \eta_r, \zeta_r) = \oint_{\Delta S_r} \mathbf{a} \cdot d\mathbf{S} + \varepsilon_r \Delta V_r,$$

where ε_r tends to zero as ΔV_r tends to zero. Addition of all these equations for $r = 1, 2, \ldots, m$ yields

$$\sum_{r=1}^{m} \Delta V_r \operatorname{div} \mathbf{a}(\xi_r, \eta_r, \zeta_r) = \sum_{r=1}^{m} \oint_{\Delta S_r} \mathbf{a} \cdot d\mathbf{S} + \sum_{r=1}^{m} \varepsilon_r \Delta V_r.$$

The boundary of each ΔV_r consists of a number of pieces which are either part of the boundary of S or part of the boundaries of two adjacent sub-regions. The total contribution from two adjacent boundary surfaces is zero since the outward normals have opposite directions over the common boundary surface.

Further, we have $\sum_{r=1}^{m} \varepsilon_r \Delta V_r \leqslant V \max \varepsilon_r$ and so this term tends to

† No confusion will ensue from the use of Δf in two different ways. It will be clear from the text when Δ is the Laplacian operator and when it refers to an increment.
Many authors use the notation ∇^2 instead of Δ for the Laplacian operator.

zero as ΔV_r tends to zero and m tends to infinity. Thus in the limit we have

$$\int_V \operatorname{div} \mathbf{a} \, dV = \oint_S \mathbf{a} . d\mathbf{S}. \tag{42.1}$$

This result, by which a volume integral is transformed into a surface integral, is known as **Gauss's theorem** or the **divergence theorem**.

Since $\operatorname{div}(f\mathbf{c}) = \mathbf{c} . \operatorname{grad} f$, where $\mathbf{c}$ is an arbitrary constant vector, the substitution $\mathbf{a} = f\mathbf{c}$ in Gauss's theorem yields

$$\mathbf{c} . \int_V \operatorname{grad} f \, dV = \mathbf{c} . \oint_S f \, d\mathbf{S}.$$

But $\mathbf{c}$ is an *arbitrary* vector and so we have

$$\int_V \operatorname{grad} f \, dV = \oint_S f \, d\mathbf{S}. \tag{42.2}$$

Choose $f = 1$ and we deduce that for a closed surface

$$\oint_S d\mathbf{S} = \mathbf{0}. \tag{42.3}$$

Let us apply Gauss's theorem to the vector field $\mathbf{a}$ defined in the volume V contained between the closed surface S and a sphere Σ of radius R, centre at the origin, and sufficiently large to enclose S completely. We have

$$\int_V \operatorname{div} \mathbf{a} \, dV = \oint_S \mathbf{a} . d\mathbf{S} + \oint_\Sigma \mathbf{a} . d\mathbf{S},$$

where the normal in the surface integrals is directed outwards from V. From equation (35.1) we have

$$\left| \oint_\Sigma \mathbf{a} . d\mathbf{S} \right| \leqslant \oint_\Sigma |\mathbf{a}| \, dS \leqslant \frac{\varepsilon}{R^2} \oint_\Sigma dS$$

if $|\mathbf{a}| \leqslant \varepsilon/R^2$ at all points on Σ. But $\oint_\Sigma dS$ is the area of the sphere of radius R and so

$$\left| \oint_\Sigma \mathbf{a} . d\mathbf{S} \right| \leqslant 4\pi\varepsilon.$$

Now let us impose the condition on $\mathbf{a}$ that $\lim_{R \to \infty} R^2 \mathbf{a} = \mathbf{0}$. Then ε can be made as small as we please and we obtain

$$\int_V \operatorname{div} \mathbf{a} \, dV = \oint_S \mathbf{a} . d\mathbf{S}.$$

That is, Gauss's theorem extends to the infinite volume outside a closed surface provided that $\lim\limits_{R\to\infty} R^2\mathbf{a} = 0$.

Example. Evaluate $\oint_S (a^2x^2+b^2y^2+c^2z^2)^{-\frac{1}{2}}\, dS$ over the surface of the ellipsoid $ax^2+by^2+cz^2=1$.

The normal to the ellipsoid is along the direction of

$$\text{grad }(ax^2+by^2+cz^2) = 2(ax\mathbf{i}+by\mathbf{j}+cz\mathbf{k}).$$

Thus the unit outward normal vector $\mathbf{n}$ to the ellipsoid is

$$\mathbf{n} = (ax\mathbf{i}+by\mathbf{j}+cz\mathbf{k})/(a^2x^2+b^2y^2+c^2z^2)^{1/2}.$$

Accordingly, the surface integral is $\oint_S \mathbf{r}\cdot d\mathbf{S}$, where $\mathbf{r}=x\mathbf{i}+y\mathbf{j}+z\mathbf{k}$ since $ax^2+by^2+cz^2=1$ on the surface.

By Gauss's theorem, the surface integral is equal to the volume integral $\int_V \text{div }\mathbf{r}\, dV = 3\int_V dV$. The volume enclosed by the ellipsoid is $4\pi/[3\sqrt{(abc)}]$ and so the original surface integral has the value

$$4\pi/\sqrt{(abc)}.$$

EXERCISES

1. Evaluate $\oint_S \mathbf{a}.d\mathbf{S}$, where $\mathbf{a}=yz\mathbf{i}+zx\mathbf{j}+xy\mathbf{k}$ and S is the surface of the cube formed by $x=0$, $x=1$, $y=0$, $y=1$, $z=0$ and $z=1$.

2. For a closed surface S containing a volume V, show that

(i) $\oint_S \mathbf{r}.d\mathbf{S}=3V$,   (ii) $\int_V \frac{1}{r^2}\, dV=\oint_S \frac{\mathbf{r}.d\mathbf{S}}{r^2}$.

3. Evaluate $\oint_S (ax^2+by^2+cz^2)\, dS$, where S is the sphere $x^2+y^2+z^2=1$.

4. Show that the value of $\oint p\left(\frac{x^4}{a^2}+\frac{y^4}{b^2}+\frac{z^4}{c^2}\right) dS$ taken over the surface of the ellipsoid $x^2/a^2+y^2/b^2+z^2/c^2=1$, where p is the perpendicular from the origin to the tangent plane at (x, y, z), is $4\pi abc(a^2+b^2+c^2)/5$.

43 Divergence of the Product of a Scalar and a Vector

Corresponding to the vector field $\mathbf{a}(x, y, z)$ and the scalar field $f(x, y, z)$, the divergence definition yields

$$\text{div }(f\mathbf{a}) = \lim_{V\to 0}\left\{\frac{1}{V}\oint_S f\mathbf{a}\cdot d\mathbf{S}\right\}.$$

Let the values of $\mathbf{a}$ and f at some fixed point inside the small region V be $\mathbf{a}_0$ and f_0. Then we may write $\mathbf{a} = \mathbf{a}_0 + \Delta\mathbf{a}$ and $f = f_0 + \Delta f$ on the surface S. Hence

$$\text{div } (f\mathbf{a}) = \lim_{V \to 0} \frac{1}{V} \oint_S (f_0 + \Delta f)\mathbf{a}.d\mathbf{S}$$

$$= \lim_{V \to 0} \frac{1}{V} \left\{ f_0 \oint_S \mathbf{a}.d\mathbf{S} + \oint_S (f - f_0)(\mathbf{a}_0 + \Delta\mathbf{a}).d\mathbf{S} \right\}$$

$$= \lim_{V \to 0} \frac{1}{V} \left\{ f_0 \oint_S \mathbf{a}.d\mathbf{S} + \mathbf{a}_0 . \oint_S f\, d\mathbf{S} \right.$$

$$\left. - f_0 \mathbf{a}_0 . \oint_S d\mathbf{S} + \oint_S \Delta f \Delta\mathbf{a}.d\mathbf{S} \right\}.$$

The last integral on the right-hand side will vanish in the limit as it is of higher order than the other terms within the braces. Further, $\oint_S d\mathbf{S} = \mathbf{0}$ by equation (42.3). Hence

$$\text{div } (f\mathbf{a}) = \lim_{V \to 0} \frac{1}{V} \left\{ f_0 \oint_S \mathbf{a}.d\mathbf{S} + \mathbf{a}_0 . \oint_S f\, d\mathbf{S} \right\}.$$

That is,

$$\text{div } (f\mathbf{a}) = f \text{ div } \mathbf{a} + \mathbf{a}.\text{grad } f. \tag{43.1}$$

This result can be obtained more easily in the special case when the basis consists of three mutually orthogonal *fixed* unit vectors. Let the basis vectors be $\mathbf{e}_1$, $\mathbf{e}_2$ and $\mathbf{e}_3$ and let $\mathbf{a} = a_1\mathbf{e}_1 + a_2\mathbf{e}_2 + a_3\mathbf{e}_3$.

From $\text{div } (f\mathbf{c}) = \mathbf{c}.\text{grad } f$ in the case of the constant vector $\mathbf{c}$, we have

$$\text{div } (f\mathbf{a}) = \sum_{r=1}^{3} \text{div } (f a_r \mathbf{e}_r)$$

$$= \sum_{r=1}^{3} \mathbf{e}_r.\text{grad } (f a_r)$$

$$= f \sum_{r=1}^{3} \mathbf{e}_r.\text{grad } a_r + \mathbf{a}.\text{grad } f.$$

Substitute $f = 1$ and obtain

$$\text{div } \mathbf{a} = \sum_{r=1}^{3} \mathbf{e}_r.\text{grad } a_r$$

and so

$$\text{div } (f\mathbf{a}) = f \text{ div } \mathbf{a} + \mathbf{a}.\text{grad } f.$$

EXERCISES

1. Obtain $f(r)$ if $\text{div } \{f(r)\mathbf{r}\} = 0$.
2. Show that $\text{div grad } (fg) = f \text{ div grad } g + g \text{ div grad } f + 2 \text{ grad } f.\text{grad } g$.

CHAPTER 8

Curl of a Vector

44 Curl of a Vector

Let $\mathbf{a}(x, y, z)$ be a vector field defined inside the region V enclosed by the surface S. We define a vector associated with $\mathbf{a}$, called the **curl** of the vector $\mathbf{a}$ and denoted by curl $\mathbf{a}$, by the relation

$$\text{curl } \mathbf{a} = -\lim_{V \to 0} \frac{\oint_S \mathbf{a} \times d\mathbf{S}}{V} \qquad (44.1)$$

provided that the limit exists.

It follows immediately from the definition that

$$\text{curl} (\lambda \mathbf{a} + \mu \mathbf{b}) = \lambda \text{ curl } \mathbf{a} + \mu \text{ curl } \mathbf{b}$$

if λ and μ are constants. If $\mathbf{c}$ is a constant vector we have

$$\text{curl} (f\mathbf{c}) = -\lim_{V \to 0} \left\{ \frac{1}{V} \oint_S f\mathbf{c} \times d\mathbf{S} \right\} = -\mathbf{c} \times \lim_{V \to 0} \left\{ \frac{1}{V} \oint_S f \, d\mathbf{S} \right\}.$$

That is,

$$\text{curl} (f\mathbf{c}) = \text{grad} f \times \mathbf{c}, \qquad (44.2)$$

from which we deduce that curl $\mathbf{c} = \mathbf{0}$.

Let $\mathbf{a} = a_i \mathbf{i} + a_j \mathbf{j} + a_k \mathbf{k}$ with respect to the fundamental system $\mathbf{i}$, $\mathbf{j}$ and $\mathbf{k}$. Then

$$\text{curl } \mathbf{a} = \text{curl} (a_i \mathbf{i}) + \text{curl} (a_j \mathbf{j}) + \text{curl} (a_k \mathbf{k})$$

$$= \text{grad } a_i \times \mathbf{i} + \text{grad } a_j \times \mathbf{j} + \text{grad } a_k \times \mathbf{k}$$

$$= \left(\frac{\partial a_i}{\partial x} \mathbf{i} + \frac{\partial a_i}{\partial y} \mathbf{j} + \frac{\partial a_i}{\partial z} \mathbf{k} \right) \times \mathbf{i} + \left(\frac{\partial a_j}{\partial x} \mathbf{i} + \frac{\partial a_j}{\partial y} \mathbf{j} + \frac{\partial a_j}{\partial z} \mathbf{k} \right) \times \mathbf{j}$$

$$+ \left(\frac{\partial a_k}{\partial x} \mathbf{i} + \frac{\partial a_k}{\partial y} \mathbf{j} + \frac{\partial a_k}{\partial z} \mathbf{k} \right) \times \mathbf{k}$$

70

$$= \left(\frac{\partial a_k}{\partial y} - \frac{\partial a_j}{\partial z}\right)\mathbf{i} + \left(\frac{\partial a_i}{\partial z} - \frac{\partial a_k}{\partial x}\right)\mathbf{j} + \left(\frac{\partial a_j}{\partial x} - \frac{\partial a_i}{\partial y}\right)\mathbf{k}.\dagger \quad (44.3)$$

We deduce that

$$\text{curl grad } f \equiv 0 \quad \text{and} \quad \text{div curl } \mathbf{a} \equiv 0$$

for arbitrary f and $\mathbf{a}$.

EXERCISES

1. If $\mathbf{a} = z\mathbf{i} - x\mathbf{j} + y\mathbf{k}$, $\mathbf{b} = y\mathbf{i} + z\mathbf{j} - x\mathbf{k}$ and $f = xyz$, calculate (i) curl $\mathbf{a}$, (ii) curl $\mathbf{b}$, (iii) curl grad f, (iv) div curl $\mathbf{a}$, (v) curl {grad $f \times (\mathbf{a} \times \mathbf{b})$}, (vi) div grad f, (vii) curl curl $(\mathbf{a} \times \mathbf{b})$.

2. Show that curl $(r^n \mathbf{r}) = 0$.

3. If $\mathbf{a} = g$ grad f, where f and g are scalar fields, show that $\mathbf{a} \cdot \text{curl } \mathbf{a} = 0$.

4. If $\boldsymbol{\lambda}$ and $\boldsymbol{\mu}$ are constant vectors, show that
(i) curl $(\boldsymbol{\lambda} \times \mathbf{r}) = 2\boldsymbol{\lambda}$, (ii) curl $\{\boldsymbol{\mu} \cdot \mathbf{r} \, \boldsymbol{\lambda}\} = \boldsymbol{\lambda} \times \boldsymbol{\mu}$, (iii) curl $\{\boldsymbol{\lambda} \times (\mathbf{r} \times \boldsymbol{\mu})\} = \boldsymbol{\mu} \times \boldsymbol{\lambda}$, (iv) curl $\{\mathbf{r} \times (\boldsymbol{\mu} \times \mathbf{r})\} = 3\mathbf{r} \times \boldsymbol{\mu}$.

5. By a method analogous to the proof of Gauss's theorem show that $\int_V \text{curl } \mathbf{a} \, dV = -\oint_S \mathbf{a} \times d\mathbf{S}$. Deduce that $\int_V \text{grad } f \, dV = \oint_S f \, d\mathbf{S}$.

6. Show that $\oint_S \mathbf{r} \times d\mathbf{S} = 0$.

7. For any scalar field f, show that
(i) $\oint_S f \text{ grad } f \times d\mathbf{S} = 0$, (ii) $\oint_S f(r)\mathbf{r} \times d\mathbf{S} = 0$.

45 Curl of the Product of a Scalar and a Vector

Corresponding to the vector field $\mathbf{a}(x, y, z)$ and the scalar field $f(x, y, z)$, the curl definition yields

$$\text{curl } (f\mathbf{a}) = -\lim_{V \to 0} \left\{ \frac{1}{V} \oint_S f\mathbf{a} \times d\mathbf{S} \right\}.$$

With the notation of Section 43 and by a similar method we obtain

$$\text{curl } (f\mathbf{a}) = -\lim_{V \to 0} \frac{1}{V} \left\{ f_0 \oint_S \mathbf{a} \times d\mathbf{S} + \mathbf{a}_0 \times \oint_S f \, d\mathbf{S} \right\}.$$

---

† This expression for curl $\mathbf{a}$ with respect to a fundamental system can be written *symbolically* in the determinantal form

$$\begin{vmatrix} \mathbf{i} & \mathbf{j} & \mathbf{k} \\ \dfrac{\partial}{\partial x} & \dfrac{\partial}{\partial y} & \dfrac{\partial}{\partial z} \\ a_i & a_j & a_k \end{vmatrix}.$$

That is,

$$\text{curl} \, (f\mathbf{a}) = f \, \text{curl} \, \mathbf{a} + \text{grad} \, f \times \mathbf{a}. \qquad (45.1)$$

EXERCISES

1. Show that curl $\{f(r)\mathbf{r}\} = 0$.
2. Calculate curl $\mathbf{b}$ in the cases when
(i) $\mathbf{b} = e^{x+y+z}(yz\mathbf{i} + zx\mathbf{j} + xy\mathbf{k})$, (ii) $\mathbf{b} = xyz(e^x \mathbf{i} + e^y \mathbf{j} + e^z \mathbf{k})$.

46 Divergence of a Vector Product

Corresponding to the vector fields $\mathbf{a}(x, y, z)$ and $\mathbf{b}(x, y, z)$, the divergence definition yields

$$\text{div} \, (\mathbf{a} \times \mathbf{b}) = \lim_{V \to 0} \left\{ \frac{1}{V} \oint_S \mathbf{a} \times \mathbf{b} \,.\, d\mathbf{S} \right\}.$$

With the notation of Section 43 and by a similar method we obtain

$$\text{div} \, (\mathbf{a} \times \mathbf{b}) = \lim_{V \to 0} \frac{1}{V} \left\{ \oint_S \mathbf{a} \times \mathbf{b}_0 \,.\, d\mathbf{S} + \oint_S \mathbf{a}_0 \times \mathbf{b} \,.\, d\mathbf{S} \right\}.$$

We have

$$\mathbf{a} \times \mathbf{b}_0 \,.\, d\mathbf{S} = -\mathbf{b}_0 \,.\, \mathbf{a} \times d\mathbf{S} \quad \text{and} \quad \mathbf{a}_0 \times \mathbf{b} \,.\, d\mathbf{S} = \mathbf{a}_0 \,.\, \mathbf{b} \times d\mathbf{S}.$$

Consequently

$$\text{div} \, (\mathbf{a} \times \mathbf{b}) = \lim_{V \to 0} \frac{1}{V} \left\{ -\mathbf{b}_0 \,.\, \oint_S \mathbf{a} \times d\mathbf{S} + \mathbf{a}_0 \,.\, \oint_S \mathbf{b} \times d\mathbf{S} \right\}$$

and so

$$\text{div} \, (\mathbf{a} \times \mathbf{b}) = \mathbf{b} \,.\, \text{curl} \, \mathbf{a} - \mathbf{a} \,.\, \text{curl} \, \mathbf{b}. \qquad (46.1)$$

EXERCISES

1. If $\mathbf{c}$ is a constant vector, show that (i) div $\left(\mathbf{c} \times \text{grad} \, \frac{1}{r} \right) = 0$,
(ii) div $\{\mathbf{c} \times f(r)\mathbf{r}\} = 0$, (iii) div $\{\mathbf{r} \times \text{grad} \, f(r)\} = 0$.
2. If λ and μ are constant vectors, show that (i) div $\{\mathbf{r} \times (\lambda \times \mathbf{r})\} = 2\mathbf{r} \times \lambda$,
(ii) div $\{(\lambda \times \mathbf{r}) \times (\mu \times \mathbf{r})\} = 2\lambda \,.\, (\mu \times \mathbf{r}) - 2\mu \,.\, (\lambda \times \mathbf{r})$.

47 The Operator a.grad

Let $\mathbf{a}(x, y, z)$ and $\mathbf{b}(x, y, z)$ be vector fields defined inside the region V enclosed by the surface S. We define the vector associated with both $\mathbf{a}$ and $\mathbf{b}$, denoted by $(\mathbf{a}.\text{grad})\mathbf{b}$, by the relation

$$(\mathbf{a}.\text{grad})\mathbf{b} = \lim_{V \to 0} \frac{\oint_S \mathbf{b}(\mathbf{a}.\,d\mathbf{S})}{V}, \qquad (47.1)$$

where $\mathbf{a}$ is to be regarded as *constant* over the surface S and provided that the limit exists.

It follows immediately from the definition that

$$(\mathbf{a}.\text{grad})(\lambda \mathbf{p} + \mu \mathbf{q}) = \lambda(\mathbf{a}.\text{grad})\mathbf{p} + \mu(\mathbf{a}.\text{grad})\mathbf{q},$$

where λ and μ are constants. Further, if $\mathbf{c}$ is a constant vector, we have

$$(\mathbf{a}.\text{grad})(f\mathbf{c}) = \lim_{V \to 0} \frac{1}{V} \oint_S f\mathbf{c}(\mathbf{a}.d\mathbf{S}) = \mathbf{c}\mathbf{a}.\lim_{V \to 0} \frac{1}{V} \oint_S f\,d\mathbf{S},$$

since $\mathbf{a}$ is constant on the surface of S. That is,

$$(\mathbf{a}.\text{grad})(f\mathbf{c}) = \mathbf{c}\,\text{grad}\,f.\mathbf{a},$$

from which we deduce that $(\mathbf{a}.\text{grad})\mathbf{c} = \mathbf{0}$.

Let $\mathbf{a} = a_i\mathbf{i} + a_j\mathbf{j} + a_k\mathbf{k}$ and $\mathbf{b} = b_i\mathbf{i} + b_j\mathbf{j} + b_k\mathbf{k}$ with respect to the fundamental system $\mathbf{i}$, $\mathbf{j}$ and $\mathbf{k}$. Then

$$\begin{aligned}
(\mathbf{a}.\text{grad})\mathbf{b} &= (\mathbf{a}.\text{grad})(b_i\mathbf{i}) + (\mathbf{a}.\text{grad})(b_j\mathbf{j}) + (\mathbf{a}.\text{grad})(b_k\mathbf{k}) \\
&= \mathbf{i}\,\text{grad}\,b_i.\mathbf{a} + \mathbf{j}\,\text{grad}\,b_j.\mathbf{a} + \mathbf{k}\,\text{grad}\,b_k.\mathbf{a} \\
&= \mathbf{i}\left(\frac{\partial b_i}{\partial x}\mathbf{i} + \frac{\partial b_i}{\partial y}\mathbf{j} + \frac{\partial b_i}{\partial z}\mathbf{k}\right).(a_i\mathbf{i} + a_j\mathbf{j} + a_k\mathbf{k}) + \text{two similar terms} \\
&= \left(a_i\frac{\partial b_i}{\partial x} + a_j\frac{\partial b_i}{\partial y} + a_k\frac{\partial b_i}{\partial z}\right)\mathbf{i} + \text{two similar terms} \\
&= a_i\frac{\partial \mathbf{b}}{\partial x} + a_j\frac{\partial \mathbf{b}}{\partial y} + a_k\frac{\partial \mathbf{b}}{\partial z}.
\end{aligned}$$

EXERCISES

1. Show that $\mathbf{a} \times \text{curl}\,\mathbf{a} = \frac{1}{2}\,\text{grad}\,\mathbf{a}^2 - (\mathbf{a}.\text{grad})\mathbf{a}$.

2. Show that $(\mathbf{a}.\text{grad})\left(\mathbf{b}.\text{grad}\,\dfrac{1}{r}\right) = \{3\mathbf{a}.\mathbf{r}\,\mathbf{b}.\mathbf{r} - r^2\mathbf{a}.\mathbf{b}\}/r^5$ if $\mathbf{a}$ and $\mathbf{b}$ are constant vectors.

48 Gradient of a Scalar Product

Corresponding to the vector fields $\mathbf{a}(x, y, z)$ and $\mathbf{b}(x, y, z)$ the gradient definition yields

$$\text{grad}\,(\mathbf{a}.\mathbf{b}) = \lim_{V \to 0} \frac{1}{V} \oint_S \mathbf{a}.\mathbf{b}\,d\mathbf{S}.$$

With the notation of Section 43 and by a similar method we obtain

$$\text{grad }(\mathbf{a}.\mathbf{b}) = \lim_{V \to 0} \frac{1}{V} \left\{ \oint_S \mathbf{a}.\mathbf{b}_0\, dS + \oint_S \mathbf{a}_0.\mathbf{b}\, dS \right\}.$$

On application of the vector triple product formulae

$$\mathbf{a}_0 \times (\mathbf{b} \times dS) = \mathbf{a}_0.dS\, \mathbf{b} - \mathbf{a}_0.\mathbf{b}\, dS,$$

$$\mathbf{b}_0 \times (\mathbf{a} \times dS) = \mathbf{b}_0.dS\, \mathbf{a} - \mathbf{a}.\mathbf{b}_0\, dS,$$

we have

$$\text{grad }(\mathbf{a}.\mathbf{b}) = \lim_{V \to 0} \frac{1}{V} \left\{ -\mathbf{b}_0 \times \oint_S \mathbf{a} \times dS - \mathbf{a}_0 \times \oint_S \mathbf{b} \times dS \right.$$
$$\left. + \oint_S \mathbf{a}(\mathbf{b}_0.dS) + \oint_S \mathbf{b}(\mathbf{a}_0.dS) \right\}.$$

Consequently

$$\text{grad }(\mathbf{a}.\mathbf{b}) = \mathbf{b} \times \text{curl }\mathbf{a} + \mathbf{a} \times \text{curl }\mathbf{b} + (\mathbf{b}.\text{grad})\mathbf{a} + (\mathbf{a}.\text{grad})\mathbf{b}. \qquad (48.1)$$

49 Curl of a Vector Product

Corresponding to the vector fields $\mathbf{a}(x, y, z)$ and $\mathbf{b}(x, y, z)$, the definition of curl yields

$$\text{curl }(\mathbf{a} \times \mathbf{b}) = -\lim_{V \to 0} \frac{1}{V} \oint_S (\mathbf{a} \times \mathbf{b}) \times dS.$$

With the notation of Section 43 and by a similar method we obtain

$$\text{curl }(\mathbf{a} \times \mathbf{b}) = -\lim_{V \to 0} \frac{1}{V} \left\{ \oint_S (\mathbf{a}_0 \times \mathbf{b}) \times dS + \oint_S (\mathbf{a} \times \mathbf{b}_0) \times dS \right\}.$$

Expanding the vector triple products we have

$$\text{curl }(\mathbf{a} \times \mathbf{b}) = -\lim_{V \to 0} \frac{1}{V} \left\{ \oint_S \mathbf{b}\mathbf{a}_0.dS - \oint_S \mathbf{a}_0\mathbf{b}.dS \right.$$
$$\left. + \oint_S \mathbf{b}_0\mathbf{a}.dS - \oint_S \mathbf{a}\mathbf{b}_0.dS \right\},$$

and so

$$\text{curl }(\mathbf{a} \times \mathbf{b}) = \mathbf{a}\, \text{div }\mathbf{b} - \mathbf{b}\, \text{div }\mathbf{a} + (\mathbf{b}.\text{grad})\mathbf{a} - (\mathbf{a}.\text{grad})\mathbf{b}. \qquad (49.1)$$

EXERCISES

1. If $\mathbf{c}$ is a constant vector, show that $\text{grad }(\mathbf{c} \times \mathbf{r}) = \mathbf{c}$.

2. If $\mathbf{c}$ is a constant vector, show that

$$\text{curl }\left(\mathbf{c} \times \text{grad}\frac{1}{r} \right) + \text{grad}\left(\mathbf{c}.\text{grad}\frac{1}{r} \right) = 0.$$

CHAPTER 9

Stokes's Theorem

50 Alternative Definition of Curl

In the curl definition (44.1) choose V to be (Fig. 32) a right circular cylinder of cross-sectional area ε and height l, where l^2 is small compared with ε. Let the unit vector in the direction of the generators of the cylinder be $\mathbf{c}$. Then

$$\mathbf{c} . \operatorname{curl} \mathbf{a} = -\lim_{V \to 0} \frac{1}{V} \oint_S \mathbf{c} . \mathbf{a} \times d\mathbf{S}$$

$$= \lim_{V \to 0} \frac{1}{V} \oint_S \mathbf{a} . \mathbf{c} \times \mathbf{n} \, dS.$$

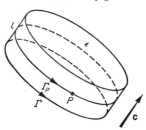

Fig. 32

The two flat ends of the cylinder make no contribution to the integral since $\mathbf{c}$ and $\mathbf{n}$ are parallel there. At a point P on the curved surface, $\mathbf{c}$ and $\mathbf{n}$ are mutually orthogonal unit vectors and so $\mathbf{c} \times \mathbf{n} = \mathbf{T}$, where $\mathbf{T}$ is the unit tangent vector to the plane section Γ_P through P parallel to an end. By convention, $\mathbf{n}$ is the *outward* normal and so the direction of Γ_P is determined by the fact that $\mathbf{c}$, $\mathbf{n}$ and $\mathbf{T}$ form a right-handed system.

We now evaluate the surface integral as a double integral. Let λ be the length along a generator measured from the base of the cylinder to P, and s be the arc length along Γ, the base curve of the cylinder. We note that Γ_P is obtained by translating Γ through a distance λ parallel to $\mathbf{c}$.

75

Since **a** depends on both s and λ, whilst **n** is independent of λ, we have

$$\oint_S \mathbf{a}.\mathbf{c} \times \mathbf{n} \, dS = \oint_\Gamma \int_{\lambda=0}^l \mathbf{a}.\mathbf{c} \times \mathbf{n} \, d\lambda \, ds$$

$$= \oint_\Gamma \mathbf{c} \times \mathbf{n}.\left[\int_0^l \mathbf{a} \, d\lambda \right] ds.$$

As l^2/ε tends to zero with ε, Taylor's expansion (Section 22) allows us to write

$$\mathbf{a}(s, \lambda) = \mathbf{a}(s, 0) + \mathbf{\eta}(s, \lambda)$$

along a generator, where $\mathbf{\eta}$ tends to zero with λ. Accordingly,

$$\int_0^l \mathbf{a} \, d\lambda = l(\mathbf{a} + \mathbf{\mu}),$$

where $\mathbf{\mu}$ is a vector function of s and l and tends to zero with l. Noting that $V = \varepsilon l$, we finally obtain

$$\mathbf{c}.\mathrm{curl}\,\mathbf{a} = \lim_{V \to 0} \frac{1}{\varepsilon l} \oint_\Gamma \mathbf{c} \times \mathbf{n}.l(\mathbf{a} + \mathbf{\mu}) \, ds$$

$$= \lim_{\varepsilon \to 0} \frac{1}{\varepsilon} \oint_\Gamma \mathbf{c} \times \mathbf{n}.\mathbf{a} \, ds$$

$$= \lim_{\varepsilon \to 0} \frac{1}{\varepsilon} \oint_\Gamma \mathbf{a}.d\mathbf{s}. \tag{50.1}$$

Accordingly, the component at a point in a direction **c** of curl **a** is the limit of the ratio of the circulation of **a** around a plane curve Γ normal to **c** and containing the point to the area enclosed by Γ.

The direction of $d\mathbf{s}$ in the circulation integral is such that **c**, the outward normal to Γ and $d\mathbf{s}$ form a right-handed system.

EXERCISES

1. Determine curl **a** in rectangular Cartesian coordinates by choosing Γ to be a rectangle in a coordinate plane.

2. If **a** is an irrotational vector, show that curl $\mathbf{a} = \mathbf{0}$. Hence deduce that curl grad $f = \mathbf{0}$ for arbitrary f.

51 Stokes's Theorem

Consider a space curve Γ bounding an open surface S. Divide S into m sub-regions so small that they may be considered to be planar with areas $\Delta S_1, \Delta S_2, \ldots, \Delta S_m$ and choose any point (ξ_r, η_r, ζ_r) inside or on the boundary Γ_r of ΔS_r (Fig. 33).

Choose a positive sense of description for Γ. Then an orientation for each Γ_r is determined by the conditions:

(i) if Γ_r and Γ have an edge in common, this edge is described in the same direction along both boundaries,

(ii) if Γ_r and $\Gamma_s(r \neq s)$ have an edge in common, this edge is described in opposite directions.

Let the unit normal at (ξ_r, η_r, ζ_r) be $\mathbf{n}_r$ with positive direction such that a right-handed corkscrew rotating in the direction of Γ_r will move in this direction.

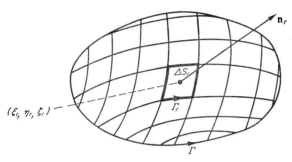

Fig. 33

From equation (50.1) we have

$$\mathbf{n}_r \cdot \mathrm{curl}\, \mathbf{a}(\xi_r, \eta_r, \zeta_r)\, \Delta S_r = \oint_{\Gamma_r} \mathbf{a}\cdot d\mathbf{s} + \varepsilon_r\, \Delta S_r,$$

where ε_r tends to zero as ΔS_r tends to zero. Addition of these equations for $r = 1, 2, \ldots, m$ yields

$$\sum_{r=1}^{m} \mathbf{n}_r \cdot \mathrm{curl}\, \mathbf{a}(\xi_r, \eta_r, \zeta_r)\, \Delta S_r = \sum_{r=1}^{m} \oint_{\Gamma_r} \mathbf{a}\cdot d\mathbf{s} + \sum_{r=1}^{m} \varepsilon_r\, \Delta S_r.$$

The boundary Γ_r of each ΔS_r consists of a number of pieces which are either part of the boundary Γ or part of the boundaries of two *adjacent* sub-regions. The contribution to the circulation from the two adjacent boundary curves is zero as they are traversed in opposite directions.

Further, we have $\sum_{r=1}^{m} \varepsilon_r\, \Delta S_r \leqslant S \max \varepsilon_r$, where S is the total area of the surface, and so this term tends to zero as m tends to infinity in such a way that each ΔS_r shrinks to a point. Hence in the limit we have

$$\int_S \mathbf{n}\cdot\mathrm{curl}\, \mathbf{a}\, dS = \oint_{\Gamma} \mathbf{a}\cdot d\mathbf{s},$$

where **n** denotes the vector field of positive unit normals to the surface S. That is,

$$\int_S \text{curl } \mathbf{a}.d\mathbf{S} = \oint_\Gamma \mathbf{a}.d\mathbf{s}. \qquad (51.1)$$

This result by which a surface integral is transformed into a line integral is known as **Stokes's theorem**.

EXERCISES

1. Verify Stokes's theorem by evaluating both integrals for the vector $y\mathbf{i} + z\mathbf{j} + x\mathbf{k}$ and the surface S given by $x^2 + y^2 + z^2 = 1$ and $z \geqslant 0$.

2. Substitute $\mathbf{a} = f\mathbf{c}$, where $\mathbf{c}$ is a constant vector, in Stokes's theorem and deduce that $\int_S \text{grad} f \times d\mathbf{S} = -\oint_\Gamma f \, d\mathbf{s}$.

3. If S is a closed region of the xy-plane bounded by a simple closed curve C, deduce from Stokes's theorem that

$$\int_S \left(\frac{\partial B}{\partial x} - \frac{\partial A}{\partial y} \right) dS = \oint_C (A \, dx + B \, dy).$$

This result is known as **Green's theorem in the plane**.

52 Surface Integral of the Curl of a Vector

Consider a closed surface S (Fig. 34) and let the closed circuit Γ divide it into two regions S_1 and S_2.

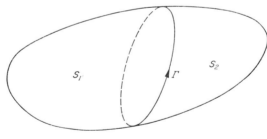

Fig. 34

Apply Stokes's theorem to both S_1 and S_2 and the results are

$$\int_{S_1} \text{curl } \mathbf{a}.d\mathbf{S} = \oint_\Gamma \mathbf{a}.d\mathbf{s}$$

and

$$\int_{S_2} \text{curl } \mathbf{a}.d\mathbf{S} = \oint_\Gamma \mathbf{a}.d\mathbf{s}.$$

The orientations of the normals to S_1 and S_2 differ, one surface having the normal in the outwards direction and the other in the inwards direction. Hence by subtraction we have

$$\oint_S \text{curl } \mathbf{a}.d\mathbf{S} = 0$$

for a *closed* surface S.

53 Curl of the Gradient of a Vector

Substitute $\mathbf{a} = \text{grad} f$, where $f(x, y, z)$ is a scalar field, in Stokes's theorem to obtain

$$\int_S \text{curl grad} f.d\mathbf{S} = \oint_\Gamma \text{grad} f.d\mathbf{s} = 0$$

in virtue of the fact that $\text{grad} f$ is always an irrotational vector as shown in Section 39. However, S is any arbitrary surface and need not be closed. It follows that

$$\text{curl grad} f \equiv \mathbf{0}$$

for any function f.

If the vector field $\mathbf{a}$ satisfies the relation curl $\mathbf{a} = \mathbf{0}$, it follows from Stokes's theorem that $\mathbf{a}$ is irrotational. In such a case we have shown (Section 39) that a scalar function $f(x, y, z)$ exists such that $\mathbf{a} = \text{grad} f$. It follows that curl $\mathbf{a} = \mathbf{0}$ implies the existence of a scalar function f for which $\mathbf{a} = \text{grad} f$.

In this proof an appeal has been made to Stokes's theorem. It follows that the region in which $\mathbf{a}$ is defined must be simply-connected.

We now show by a counterexample that the vector field $\mathbf{a}$ may not be irrotational if curl $\mathbf{a} = 0$ in a region which is not simply-connected.

Consider the vector

$$\mathbf{a} = -\frac{y}{x^2+y^2}\mathbf{i} + \frac{x}{x^2+y^2}\mathbf{j}.$$

This vector $\mathbf{a}$ is not defined at the origin but is defined in the multiply-connected region between any two spheres with centres at the origin. In this region we readily verify that curl $\mathbf{a} = 0$.

The line-integral of $\mathbf{a}$ round any closed circuit Γ is given by

$$I = \oint_\Gamma \left(\frac{-y\mathbf{i}+x\mathbf{j}}{x^2+y^2}\right)(dx\mathbf{i}+dy\mathbf{j})$$

$$= \oint_\Gamma \frac{x\,dy-y\,dx}{x^2+y^2} = \oint_\Gamma d\left(\tan^{-1}\frac{x}{y}\right).$$

Select Γ to be the circle $x^2 + y^2 = \rho^2$, $z = 0$. The substitution $x = \rho \cos \psi$, $y = \rho \sin \psi$ yields

$$I = \int_0^{2\pi} d\psi = 2\pi \neq 0$$

and so **a** is not irrotational.

EXERCISE

1. If the vector field **a** is irrotational in the region V enclosed by the surface S and if **a** is along the surface normal on S, show that

$$\int_V \mathbf{a} \times \operatorname{grad} f \, dV = \mathbf{0}$$

for any scalar field f.

54   Divergence of the Curl of a Vector

Replace the vector **a** by curl **a** in Gauss's theorem, equation (42.1), and the result is

$$\int_V \operatorname{div} \operatorname{curl} \mathbf{a} \, dV = \oint_S \operatorname{curl} \mathbf{a} . d\mathbf{S} = 0$$

since S is a closed surface. The volume integral is zero over any arbitrary region and so we have

$$\operatorname{div} \operatorname{curl} \mathbf{a} \equiv 0$$

for any vector **a**.

55   Solenoidal Vectors

A vector field **a** is said to be **solenoidal** if div **a** = 0. Since

$$\operatorname{div} \operatorname{curl} \mathbf{a} \equiv 0$$

for all vectors **a**, it is clear that curl **a** is always a solenoidal vector. We now establish by a method due to L. Brandt† the converse result that corresponding to a solenoidal vector field **a** there exists a vector field **b** such that **a** = curl **b**.

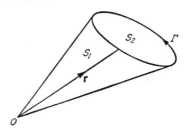

Fig. 35

† *Amer. Math. Monthly*, **57**, 161 (1950).

Consider the closed surface S formed by a cone with vertex at O and plane base (Fig. 35) determined by the closed circuit Γ. Since div $\mathbf{a} = 0$, Gauss's theorem yields

$$\int_S \mathbf{a} \cdot d\mathbf{S} = 0.$$

Let us denote the curved surface by S_1, the flat base by S_2 and the equation of Γ by $\mathbf{r} = \mathbf{r}(s)$, where s measures arc distance along Γ and $\mathbf{r}$ has its initial point at O. The equation of S_1 is $\mathbf{R} = \lambda \mathbf{r}(s)$ for the range $0 \leqslant \lambda \leqslant 1$. The vector element of area $d\mathbf{S}$ in the direction of the external normal to S_1 is given by

$$d\mathbf{S} = \frac{\partial \mathbf{R}}{\partial s} \times \frac{\partial \mathbf{R}}{\partial \lambda} \, ds \, d\lambda = \lambda \mathbf{T} \times \mathbf{r} \, ds \, d\lambda,$$

where $\mathbf{T}$ is the unit tangent vector to Γ. Thus

$$\int_{S_1} \mathbf{a} \cdot d\mathbf{S} = \iint_{S_1} \lambda \mathbf{a}(\lambda \mathbf{r}) \cdot \mathbf{T} \times \mathbf{r} \, ds \, d\lambda$$

$$= \oint_\Gamma \left[\int_0^1 \lambda \mathbf{a}(\lambda \mathbf{r}) \, d\lambda \right] \cdot \mathbf{T} \times \mathbf{r} \, ds$$

$$= \oint_\Gamma \mathbf{r} \times \left[\int_0^1 \lambda \mathbf{a}(\lambda \mathbf{r}) \, d\lambda \right] \cdot d\mathbf{s}.$$

By application of Stokes's theorem on the assumption that $\mathbf{a} = \text{curl } \mathbf{b}$ we have

$$\int_{S_2} \mathbf{a} \cdot d\mathbf{S} = \int_{S_2} \text{curl } \mathbf{b} \cdot d\mathbf{S} = \oint_\Gamma \mathbf{b} \cdot d\mathbf{s}.$$

Accordingly

$$0 = \oint_S \mathbf{a} \cdot d\mathbf{S} = \oint_\Gamma \mathbf{p} \cdot d\mathbf{s},$$

where

$$\mathbf{p} = \mathbf{b} + \mathbf{r} \times \int_0^1 \lambda \mathbf{a}(\lambda \mathbf{r}) \, d\lambda.$$

Thus the vector field $\mathbf{p}$ is irrotational and a scalar function $f(x, y, z)$ exists such that $\mathbf{p} = \text{grad } f$. Hence

$$\mathbf{b} = \text{grad } f - \mathbf{r} \times \int_0^1 \lambda \mathbf{a}(\lambda \mathbf{r}) \, d\lambda. \tag{55.1}$$

That is, we have obtained a vector $\mathbf{b}$ for which $\mathbf{a} = \text{curl } \mathbf{b}$. Note that $\mathbf{b}$ is indeterminate to the extent that we may add the gradient of any scalar function. We call $\mathbf{b}$ a **vector potential** of the solenoidal vector $\mathbf{a}$.

Example. Show that the vector $\mathbf{a} = z\mathbf{i} + x\mathbf{j} + y\mathbf{k}$ is solenoidal and obtain a vector potential for it.

Clearly div $\mathbf{a} = 0$ and so $\mathbf{a}$ is solenoidal. Application of equation (55.1) shows that a vector potential is

$$-\mathbf{r} \times \int_0^1 \lambda(\lambda z\mathbf{i} + \lambda x\mathbf{j} + \lambda y\mathbf{k})\, d\lambda$$

$$= -\tfrac{1}{3}(x\mathbf{i} + y\mathbf{j} + z\mathbf{k}) \times (z\mathbf{i} + x\mathbf{j} + y\mathbf{k})$$

$$= \tfrac{1}{3}\{(zx - y^2)\mathbf{i} + (xy - z^2)\mathbf{j} + (yz - x^2)\mathbf{k}\}.$$

EXERCISES

1. Show that the vector $\operatorname{grad} f \times \operatorname{grad} g$ corresponding to the scalar fields f and g is solenoidal.

2. Show that the following vectors are solenoidal and obtain vector potentials: (i) $(y-z)\mathbf{i} + (z-x)\mathbf{j} + (x-y)\mathbf{k}$, (ii) $r^3\mathbf{c} \times \mathbf{r}$, where $\mathbf{c}$ is a constant vector, (iii) $yz\mathbf{i} + zx\mathbf{j} + xy\mathbf{k}$, (iv) $e^x\mathbf{j}$.

3. If the vector field $\mathbf{a}$ is both irrotational and solenoidal, show that $\operatorname{grad}(\mathbf{a}.\mathbf{c}) = \operatorname{curl}(\mathbf{a} \times \mathbf{c})$ for any constant vector $\mathbf{c}$.

4. If the vector field $\mathbf{a}$ is solenoidal in the region V enclosed by the surface S and if the component of $\mathbf{a}$ along the surface normal vanishes, show that $\int_V \mathbf{a}.\operatorname{grad} f\, dV = 0$ for any scalar field f.

5. If the vector field $\mathbf{a}$ is solenoidal, show that $2\int_V \mathbf{r}.\mathbf{a}\, dV = \oint_S r^2\mathbf{a}.d\mathbf{S}$.

CHAPTER 10

Green's Theorems

56 Green's Theorems

In the relation $\operatorname{div}(f\mathbf{a}) = f\operatorname{div}\mathbf{a} + \mathbf{a}.\operatorname{grad} f$ let us write $\mathbf{a} = \operatorname{grad} g$, where $g(x, y, z)$ is a scalar field. Then

$$\operatorname{div}(f\operatorname{grad} g) = f\operatorname{div}(\operatorname{grad} g) + \operatorname{grad} g.\operatorname{grad} f$$
$$= f\Delta g + \operatorname{grad} f.\operatorname{grad} g.$$

Integrate over the region V contained by the closed surface S and we obtain

$$\int_V \operatorname{div}(f\operatorname{grad} g)\, dV = \int_V f\Delta g\, dV + \int_V \operatorname{grad} f.\operatorname{grad} g\, dV.$$

The integral on the left-hand side of this equation is $\oint_S f\operatorname{grad} g.d\mathbf{S}$

by Gauss's theorem. However,

$$f\operatorname{grad} g.d\mathbf{S} = f\operatorname{grad} g.\mathbf{n}\, dS = f\frac{\partial g}{\partial n}\, dS$$

and so we obtain

$$\oint_S f\frac{\partial g}{\partial n}\, dS = \int_V f\Delta g\, dV + \int_V \operatorname{grad} f.\operatorname{grad} g\, dV. \qquad (56.1)$$

We deduce that

$$\oint_S f\frac{\partial f}{\partial n}\, dS = \int_V f\Delta f\, dV + \int_V (\operatorname{grad} f)^2\, dV \qquad (56.2)$$

and

$$\oint_S \left(f\frac{\partial g}{\partial n} - g\frac{\partial f}{\partial n}\right) dS = \int_V (f\Delta g - g\Delta f)\, dV. \qquad (56.3)$$

These relations are generally known as **Green's theorems.**

57 Harmonic Functions

A scalar function φ is said to be harmonic if it satisfies Laplace's equation $\Delta\varphi = 0$.

Let φ_1 and φ_2 be two harmonic functions in the region V enclosed by the surface S such that $\varphi_1 = \varphi_2$ on S. Then $f = \varphi_1 - \varphi_2$ is harmonic in V and vanishes on S. Application of the equation (56.2) yields

$$\int_V (\operatorname{grad} f)^2 \, dV = 0.$$

Hence $\operatorname{grad} f = \mathbf{0}$ in V. That is, f is constant in V. But f is zero on S and so $f = 0$ in V. That is, $\varphi_1 = \varphi_2$ in V.

Consequently, a harmonic function in a region bounded by a closed surface is uniquely determined by its values on the boundary.

Substitute $f = 1$ and $g = \varphi$ in equation (56.3) when φ is harmonic. The result is

$$\oint_S \frac{\partial\varphi}{\partial n} \, dS = 0. \tag{57.1}$$

That is, the surface integral of the normal derivative of a harmonic function is zero over the bounding surface of the region in which it is harmonic.

EXERCISES

1. If φ is harmonic in the region V enclosed by the surface S and φ is constant on S, show that φ is constant in V.

2. If φ_1 and φ_2 are both harmonic in the region V enclosed by the surface S and their normal derivatives are equal on S, show that $\varphi_1 - \varphi_2$ is constant in V.

58 Uniqueness Theorem

We now prove that there can be at most one vector field in a region V contained by a closed surface S, if the divergence and curl are given everywhere in V and the component of the vector in the direction of the normal to the surface is given on S.

Suppose $\mathbf{a}$ and $\mathbf{b}$ are two vectors satisfying the given conditions. Form the vector $\mathbf{p} = \mathbf{a} - \mathbf{b}$ and we have

$$\operatorname{div} \mathbf{p} = 0 \quad \text{and} \quad \operatorname{curl} \mathbf{p} = \mathbf{0} \text{ in } V$$

and

$$\mathbf{p} \cdot \mathbf{n} = 0 \text{ on } S.$$

Since curl $\mathbf{p}=0$, the vector $\mathbf{p}$ is irrotational and thus a scalar field $f(x, y, z)$ exists such that

$$\mathbf{p} = \operatorname{grad} f.$$

Accordingly

$$\Delta f = \operatorname{div} \operatorname{grad} f = \operatorname{div} \mathbf{p} = 0 \qquad \text{in } V$$

and

$$\frac{\partial f}{\partial n} = \operatorname{grad} f . \mathbf{n} = \mathbf{p} . \mathbf{n} = 0 \qquad \text{on } S.$$

Application of equation (56.2) yields

$$\int_V (\operatorname{grad} f)^2 \, dV = 0.$$

The integrand is never negative and so we have $(\operatorname{grad} f)^2 = 0$. That is, $\mathbf{p} = \operatorname{grad} f = 0$. Hence $\mathbf{a} = \mathbf{b}$ as required.

Note carefully that we have not shown that a vector field exists satisfying the given conditions. We have merely shown that if one such vector field exists, then it is unique.

59   Solid Angle

Form the cone joining the point O to the points of a closed curve Γ. The solid angle of the cone is defined to be the surface area of the unit sphere, with centre at O, intercepted by the cone.

Consider the vector

$$\mathbf{a} = \operatorname{grad} \frac{1}{r} = -\frac{1}{r^2} \operatorname{grad} r = -\frac{1}{r^3} \mathbf{r}, \qquad (r \neq 0),$$

where $\mathbf{r}$ refers to O as initial point. Further, in virtue of equation (43.1) we have $\operatorname{div} (f\mathbf{b}) = f \operatorname{div} \mathbf{b} + \mathbf{b} . \operatorname{grad} f$ and so for $r \neq 0$ we have

$$\operatorname{div} \mathbf{a} = -\operatorname{div}\left(\frac{1}{r^3} \mathbf{r}\right) = -\frac{1}{r^3} \operatorname{div} \mathbf{r} - \mathbf{r} . \operatorname{grad}\left(\frac{1}{r^3}\right) = -\frac{3}{r^3} + \mathbf{r} . \left(\frac{3}{r^4} \frac{\mathbf{r}}{r}\right) = 0.$$

Apply Gauss's theorem, equation (42.1), to the region (Fig. 36) of the cone bounded by the curved surface G formed by the generators, an open surface S whose boundary is Γ and the portion σ of the *small* sphere of radius ρ intercepted by the cone. (We emphasize that ρ will not tend to zero. We choose ρ sufficiently small so that the surfaces S and σ do not intersect.) The result is

$$\int_S \operatorname{grad} \frac{1}{r} . d\mathbf{S} + \int_\sigma \operatorname{grad} \frac{1}{r} . d\mathbf{S} + \int_G \operatorname{grad} \frac{1}{r} . d\mathbf{S} = 0.$$

On G we have $\operatorname{grad}\dfrac{1}{r}=-\dfrac{1}{r^3}\,\mathbf{r}$ and $\mathbf{r}$ is orthogonal to the surface

normal $\mathbf{n}$. Accordingly, $\displaystyle\int_G \operatorname{grad}\frac{1}{r}.d\mathbf{S}=0$. On σ we have $r=\rho$ and

$\mathbf{n}=-\mathbf{r}/\rho$, the sign being negative because the normal is outwards from the surface, and so

$$\int_\sigma \operatorname{grad}\frac{1}{r}.d\mathbf{S} = \int_\sigma \frac{\mathbf{r}}{r^3}.\frac{\mathbf{r}}{\rho}\,dS = \frac{1}{\rho^2}\int_\sigma dS.$$

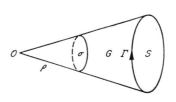

Fig. 36

But the solid angle Ω of the cone is given by $\displaystyle\int dS$ taken over the

portion of the unit sphere intercepted by the cone. Hence $\displaystyle\int_\sigma dS=\rho^2\Omega$

and so $\displaystyle\int_\sigma \operatorname{grad}\frac{1}{r}.d\mathbf{S}=\Omega.$ Thus we obtain

$$\Omega = -\int_S \operatorname{grad}\frac{1}{r}.d\mathbf{S}.$$

As a corollary, it follows for a closed surface S that

$$\oint_S \operatorname{grad}\frac{1}{r}.d\mathbf{S} = -4\pi \quad \text{if } O \text{ is inside } S,$$

$$= 0 \quad \text{if } O \text{ is outside } S.$$

EXERCISE

1. Show that the solid angle subtended at the origin by a closed curve Γ is given by $\pm\displaystyle\oint_\Gamma \frac{z(y\,dx-x\,dy)}{(x^2+y^2)(x^2+y^2+z^2)^{1/2}}.$

60 Green's Identity

We apply equation (56.3) with $g=\dfrac{1}{r}$, where r is the distance from a fixed point O, to the region V contained by the closed surface S. In virtue of the result $\Delta g = \operatorname{div} \operatorname{grad} \dfrac{1}{r} = 0$ established in the preceding section we have

$$\oint_S \left[f \frac{\partial}{\partial n} \left(\frac{1}{r} \right) - \frac{1}{r} \frac{\partial f}{\partial n} \right] dS + \int_V \frac{\Delta f}{r} \, dV = 0.$$

Consider the case when O lies inside the surface S. We exclude O by surrounding it with a small sphere σ of radius ε. Then we have

$$\oint_S \left[f \frac{\partial}{\partial n} \left(\frac{1}{r} \right) - \frac{1}{r} \frac{\partial f}{\partial n} \right] dS + \oint_\sigma \left[f \frac{\partial}{\partial n} \left(\frac{1}{r} \right) - \frac{1}{r} \frac{\partial f}{\partial n} \right] dS + \int_{\overline{V}} \frac{\Delta f}{r} \, dV = 0,$$

where $\overline{V}$ is the region contained between σ and S.

On the surface σ we have $r = \varepsilon$ and the external normal is directed towards O. Thus we have $\dfrac{\partial f}{\partial n} = -\dfrac{\partial f}{\partial r}$ whilst

$$\frac{\partial}{\partial n} \left(\frac{1}{r} \right) = -\frac{d}{dr} \left(\frac{1}{r} \right) = \frac{1}{r^2} = \frac{1}{\varepsilon^2}.$$

Further, $dS = \varepsilon^2 \, d\Omega$, where $d\Omega$ is the solid angle subtended by dS at O. Hence

$$\oint_\sigma \left[f \frac{\partial}{\partial n} \left(\frac{1}{r} \right) - \frac{1}{r} \frac{\partial f}{\partial n} \right] dS = \oint_\sigma \left[\frac{f}{\varepsilon^2} + \frac{1}{\varepsilon} \frac{\partial f}{\partial r} \right] \varepsilon^2 \, d\Omega$$

$$= \oint_\sigma \left(f + \varepsilon \frac{\partial f}{\partial r} \right) d\Omega$$

$$\to 4\pi f_0 \quad \text{as} \quad \varepsilon \to 0,$$

where f_0 denotes the value of f at O. Let ε tend to zero; the result is **Green's identity**

$$f_0 = -\frac{1}{4\pi} \oint_S \left[f \frac{\partial}{\partial n} \left(\frac{1}{r} \right) - \frac{1}{r} \frac{\partial f}{\partial n} \right] dS - \frac{1}{4\pi} \int_V \frac{\Delta f}{r} \, dV. \quad (60.1)$$

If O is outside the region V contained by S, equation (56.3) immediately yields

$$\oint_S \left[f \frac{\partial}{\partial n} \left(\frac{1}{r} \right) - \frac{1}{r} \frac{\partial f}{\partial n} \right] dS + \int_V \frac{\Delta f}{r} \, dV = 0.$$

Consider the case when the function f is harmonic, that is $\Delta f = 0$. We deduce from (60.1) that

$$f_0 = -\frac{1}{4\pi} \oint_S \left[f \frac{\partial}{\partial n} \left(\frac{1}{r} \right) - \frac{1}{r} \frac{\partial f}{\partial n} \right] dS.$$

Accordingly, the values of a harmonic function f and its normal derivative $\frac{\partial f}{\partial n}$ at all points on the boundary S of a closed region determine the value of the function at all interior points.

It can be shown that either a knowledge of f or $\frac{\partial f}{\partial n}$ on S determines the other when f is harmonic. Consequently this result has little practical value.

Further, consider the cases when S is a sphere with centre at 0.

Since $\frac{\partial}{\partial n}\left(\frac{1}{r}\right) = -\frac{1}{r^2}$ we have in virtue of (57.1) that

$$f_0 = \frac{1}{4\pi r^2} \oint_S f \, dS.$$

That is, if a function is harmonic in a spherical region, its value at the centre is the arithmetic mean of its values on the surface of the sphere. It can be shown that a function with this property is harmonic.

In Section 42 we saw that Gauss's theorem can be extended to the infinite volume outside a closed surface provided that $\lim_{R \to \infty} R^2 a = 0$. In the same way Green's theorems can be extended to the infinite volume provided that $\lim_{R \to \infty} R^2 f \operatorname{grad} g = \lim_{R \to \infty} R^2 g \operatorname{grad} f = 0$. Corresponding to $g = \frac{1}{r}$ we have $\operatorname{grad} g = -\frac{1}{r^3} \mathbf{r}$ and these conditions are $\lim_{r \to \infty} (-f\mathbf{r})/r = \lim_{r \to \infty} r \operatorname{grad} f = 0$.

Thus, under these conditions, we may apply Green's identity to the case when V is the region outside the closed surface S containing the point O. Now let S shrink to the point O and we obtain

$$f_0 = -\frac{1}{4\pi} \int \frac{\Delta f}{r} \, dV,$$

where the volume integral is taken over the whole of space.

CHAPTER 11

Orthogonal Curvilinear Coordinates

61 Curvilinear Coordinates

Let us change from rectangular Cartesian coordinates x, y and z to curvilinear coordinates u, v and w by means of the three equations

$$x = f(u, v, w), \quad y = g(u, v, w), \quad z = h(u, v, w),$$

where f, g and h are single-valued functions with continuous partial derivatives of the first order in some given region. The functions f, g and h must be independent and the condition for this is that the Jacobian determinant

$$\frac{\partial(x, y, z)}{\partial(u, v, w)} \equiv \begin{vmatrix} \dfrac{\partial x}{\partial u} & \dfrac{\partial x}{\partial v} & \dfrac{\partial x}{\partial w} \\[2mm] \dfrac{\partial y}{\partial u} & \dfrac{\partial y}{\partial v} & \dfrac{\partial y}{\partial w} \\[2mm] \dfrac{\partial z}{\partial u} & \dfrac{\partial z}{\partial v} & \dfrac{\partial z}{\partial w} \end{vmatrix} \neq 0.$$

In practice this condition may not apply at some points and particular care may be necessary there.

Under the given conditions it can be shown that u, v and w can be obtained as single-valued functions of x, y and z with continuous partial derivatives of the first order.

If one of the coordinates u, v and w is held fixed and the other two allowed to vary, the point (x, y, z) traces out a surface called a **coordinate surface**. There are three families of such surfaces corresponding to constant values of u, v and w.

If two of the coordinates u, v and w are held fixed and the third coordinate allowed to vary, the point (x, y, z) traces out a curve called a **coordinate curve**. There are three families of such curves corresponding to varying u, v and w respectively. Each coordinate curve is the intersection of two coordinate surfaces. For example, the curve corresponding to varying u is the intersection of the surfaces corresponding to fixed v and w.

Let P be given by the position vector $\mathbf{r} = x\mathbf{i} + y\mathbf{j} + z\mathbf{k}$ where $\mathbf{i}$, $\mathbf{j}$ and $\mathbf{k}$ form a fundamental system. The change of coordinates to u, v, w makes $\mathbf{r}$ a function of u, v and w. Then the vectors $\dfrac{\partial \mathbf{r}}{\partial u}$, $\dfrac{\partial \mathbf{r}}{\partial v}$, $\dfrac{\partial \mathbf{r}}{\partial w}$ are tangent to the coordinate curves. Denoting the *unit* vectors tangent to the coordinate curves by $\mathbf{I}$, $\mathbf{J}$ and $\mathbf{K}$, we have

$$\frac{\partial \mathbf{r}}{\partial u} = h_1 \mathbf{I}, \quad \frac{\partial \mathbf{r}}{\partial v} = h_2 \mathbf{J}, \quad \frac{\partial \mathbf{r}}{\partial w} = h_3 \mathbf{K},$$

where

$$h_1 = \left|\frac{\partial \mathbf{r}}{\partial u}\right|, \quad h_2 = \left|\frac{\partial \mathbf{r}}{\partial v}\right|, \quad h_3 = \left|\frac{\partial \mathbf{r}}{\partial w}\right|.$$

62 Orthogonal Curvilinear Coordinates

We shall now impose the restriction that the coordinate curves are mutually orthogonal. In this case we refer to an **orthogonal curvilinear** coordinate system and the vectors $\mathbf{I}$, $\mathbf{J}$ and $\mathbf{K}$ satisfy the relations

$$\mathbf{J}.\mathbf{K} = \mathbf{K}.\mathbf{I} = \mathbf{I}.\mathbf{J} = 0.$$

Further, we have

$$d\mathbf{r} = \frac{\partial \mathbf{r}}{\partial u} du + \frac{\partial \mathbf{r}}{\partial v} dv + \frac{\partial \mathbf{r}}{\partial w} dw$$

$$= h_1 \, du\mathbf{I} + h_2 \, dv\mathbf{J} + h_3 \, dw\mathbf{K}$$

and so the length ds of arc between the neighbouring points (u, v, w) and $(u+du, v+dv, w+dw)$ is given by

$$ds^2 = d\mathbf{r}.d\mathbf{r} = h_1^2 \, du^2 + h_2^2 \, dv^2 + h_3^2 \, dw^2,$$

since $\mathbf{I}$, $\mathbf{J}$, $\mathbf{K}$ form an orthogonal system of unit vectors.

The arc lengths ds_1, ds_2 and ds_3 along the coordinate curves are given by

$$ds_1 = h_1 \, du, \quad ds_2 = h_2 \, dv, \quad ds_3 = h_3 \, dw.$$

Example 1. Obtain h_1, h_2, h_3 and the vectors $\mathbf{I}$, $\mathbf{J}$, $\mathbf{K}$ for the cylindrical coordinate system given by $x = u \cos v$, $y = u \sin v$, $z = w$.

The ranges of u, v and w are given by $u \geqslant 0$, $0 \leqslant v < 2\pi$ and $-\infty < w < \infty$.

We have
$$\mathbf{r} = u \cos v \, \mathbf{i} + u \sin v \, \mathbf{j} + w\mathbf{k}.$$
Thus
$$\frac{\partial \mathbf{r}}{\partial u} = \cos v \, \mathbf{i} + \sin v \, \mathbf{j}, \qquad \left| \frac{\partial \mathbf{r}}{\partial u} \right| = 1,$$

$$\frac{\partial \mathbf{r}}{\partial v} = -u \sin v \, \mathbf{i} + u \cos v \, \mathbf{j}, \qquad \left| \frac{\partial \mathbf{r}}{\partial v} \right| = u,$$

$$\frac{\partial \mathbf{r}}{\partial w} = \mathbf{k}, \qquad\qquad\qquad \left| \frac{\partial \mathbf{r}}{\partial w} \right| = 1.$$

Hence
$$h_1 = 1, \quad h_2 = u, \quad h_3 = 1$$
and
$$\mathbf{I} = \cos v \, \mathbf{i} + \sin v \, \mathbf{j}, \quad \mathbf{J} = -\sin v \, \mathbf{i} + \cos v \, \mathbf{j}, \quad \mathbf{K} = \mathbf{k}.$$

Example 2. Obtain h_1, h_2, h_3 and the vectors $\mathbf{I}$, $\mathbf{J}$, $\mathbf{K}$ for the spherical polar coordinate system given by $x = u \sin v \cos w$, $y = u \sin v \sin w$, $z = u \cos v$.

Here the ranges of u, v and w are given by $u \geqslant 0$, $0 \leqslant v \leqslant \pi$ and $0 \leqslant w < 2\pi$. We have
$$\mathbf{r} = u \sin v \cos w \, \mathbf{i} + u \sin v \sin w \, \mathbf{j} + u \cos v \, \mathbf{k}.$$
Thus
$$\frac{\partial \mathbf{r}}{\partial u} = \sin v \cos w \, \mathbf{i} + \sin v \sin w \, \mathbf{j} + \cos v \, \mathbf{k}, \qquad \left| \frac{\partial \mathbf{r}}{\partial u} \right| = 1,$$

$$\frac{\partial \mathbf{r}}{\partial v} = u \cos v \cos w \, \mathbf{i} + u \cos v \sin w \, \mathbf{j} - u \sin v \, \mathbf{k}, \quad \left| \frac{\partial \mathbf{r}}{\partial v} \right| = u,$$

$$\frac{\partial \mathbf{r}}{\partial w} = -u \sin v \sin w \, \mathbf{i} + u \sin v \cos w \, \mathbf{j}, \qquad\qquad \left| \frac{\partial \mathbf{r}}{\partial w} \right| = u \sin v.$$

Hence
$$h_1 = 1, \quad h_2 = u, \quad h_3 = u \sin v$$
and
$$\mathbf{I} = \sin v \cos w \, \mathbf{i} + \sin v \sin w \, \mathbf{j} + \cos v \, \mathbf{k},$$
$$\mathbf{J} = \cos v \cos w \, \mathbf{i} + \cos v \sin w \, \mathbf{j} - \sin v \, \mathbf{k},$$
$$\mathbf{K} = -\sin w \, \mathbf{i} + \cos w \, \mathbf{j}.$$

EXERCISE

1. Obtain h_1, h_2, h_3 and the vectors $\mathbf{I}$, $\mathbf{J}$, $\mathbf{K}$ for the following coordinate systems:

(i) parabolic cylindrical coordinates given by

$$x = \tfrac{1}{2}(u^2 - v^2), \quad y = uv, \quad z = w,$$

(ii) paraboloidal coordinates given by

$$x = uv \cos w, \, y = uv \sin w, \, z = \tfrac{1}{2}(u^2 - v^2),$$

(iii) prolate ellipsoidal coordinates given by

$$x = a\sqrt{\{(u^2-1)(1-v^2)\}} \cos w, \quad y = a\sqrt{\{(u^2-1)(1-v^2)\}} \sin w,$$
$$z = auv.$$

63 Gradient

In Section 38 it was proved that

$$\operatorname{grad} f = \frac{\partial f}{\partial s_1} \mathbf{I} + \frac{\partial f}{\partial s_2} \mathbf{J} + \frac{\partial f}{\partial s_3} \mathbf{K}.$$

However, the directional derivative $\partial f / \partial s_1$ is given by

$$\frac{\partial f}{\partial s_1} = \lim_{\Delta u \to 0} \frac{f(u + \Delta u, v, w) - f(u, v, w)}{h_1 \Delta u} = \frac{1}{h_1} \frac{\partial f}{\partial u}.$$

Similarly $\dfrac{\partial f}{\partial s_2} = \dfrac{1}{h_2} \dfrac{\partial f}{\partial v}$ and $\dfrac{\partial f}{\partial s_3} = \dfrac{1}{h_3} \dfrac{\partial f}{\partial w}$ and so

$$\operatorname{grad} f = \frac{1}{h_1} \frac{\partial f}{\partial u} \mathbf{I} + \frac{1}{h_2} \frac{\partial f}{\partial v} \mathbf{J} + \frac{1}{h_3} \frac{\partial f}{\partial w} \mathbf{K}. \tag{63.1}$$

From this result we see that

$$\operatorname{grad} u = \frac{1}{h_1} \mathbf{I}, \quad \operatorname{grad} v = \frac{1}{h_2} \mathbf{J}, \quad \operatorname{grad} w = \frac{1}{h_3} \mathbf{K}.$$

Hence

$$\left. \begin{array}{l} \mathbf{I} = \mathbf{J} \times \mathbf{K} = h_2 h_3 \operatorname{grad} v \times \operatorname{grad} w, \\ \mathbf{J} = \mathbf{K} \times \mathbf{I} = h_3 h_1 \operatorname{grad} w \times \operatorname{grad} u, \\ \mathbf{K} = \mathbf{I} \times \mathbf{J} = h_1 h_2 \operatorname{grad} u \times \operatorname{grad} v. \end{array} \right\} \tag{63.2}$$

Using the results of examples 1 and 2 of the previous section, we have that grad f in cylindrical and spherical polar coordinates is given by

$$\frac{\partial f}{\partial u} \mathbf{I} + \frac{1}{u} \frac{\partial f}{\partial v} \mathbf{J} + \frac{\partial f}{\partial w} \mathbf{K}$$

and

$$\frac{\partial f}{\partial u} \mathbf{I} + \frac{1}{u} \frac{\partial f}{\partial v} \mathbf{J} + \frac{1}{u \sin v} \frac{\partial f}{\partial w} \mathbf{K}$$

respectively.

EXERCISE

1. Obtain grad f in the following coordinate systems: (i) parabolic cylindrical coordinates, (ii) paraboloidal coordinates, (iii) prolate ellipsoidal coordinates.

64 Divergence

Consider the vector $\mathbf{a}=a_I\mathbf{I}+a_J\mathbf{J}+a_K\mathbf{K}$, where the a_I, a_J and a_K are now components with respect to the basis $\mathbf{I}$, $\mathbf{J}$, $\mathbf{K}$. From

$$\text{div } (f\mathbf{a}) = f \text{ div } \mathbf{a}+\mathbf{a}.\text{grad } f$$

we have in virtue of (63.2) that

$$\text{div } (a_I\mathbf{I}) = \text{div } (a_I h_2 h_3 \text{ grad } v \times \text{grad } w)$$
$$= a_I h_2 h_3 \text{ div } (\text{grad } v \times \text{grad } w)+\text{grad } v \times \text{grad } w.\text{grad } (a_I h_2 h_3).$$

But $\text{div } (\mathbf{a}\times\mathbf{b})=\mathbf{b}.\text{curl } \mathbf{a}-\mathbf{a}.\text{curl } \mathbf{b}$ and $\text{curl grad} f=\mathbf{0}$. Hence

$$\text{div } (a_I\mathbf{I}) = \text{grad } v \times \text{grad } w.\text{grad } (a_I h_2 h_3)$$
$$= \frac{1}{h_2 h_3}\mathbf{J}\times\mathbf{K}.\left[\frac{1}{h_1}\frac{\partial(a_I h_2 h_3)}{\partial u}\mathbf{I}+\frac{1}{h_2}\frac{\partial(a_I h_2 h_3)}{\partial v}\mathbf{J}\right.$$
$$\left.+\frac{1}{h_3}\frac{\partial(a_I h_2 h_3)}{\partial w}\mathbf{K}\right]$$
$$= \frac{1}{h_1 h_2 h_3}\frac{\partial}{\partial u} (a_I h_2 h_3).$$

Adding the corresponding results for $\text{div } (a_J\mathbf{J})$ and $\text{div } (a_K\mathbf{K})$ we have

$$\text{div } \mathbf{a} = \frac{1}{h_1 h_2 h_3}\left[\frac{\partial}{\partial u} (a_I h_2 h_3)+\frac{\partial}{\partial v} (a_J h_3 h_1)+\frac{\partial}{\partial w} (a_K h_1 h_2)\right]. \quad (64.1)$$

In particular, the corresponding results for cylindrical and spherical polar coordinates are

$$\frac{1}{u}\left[\frac{\partial}{\partial u} (ua_I)+\frac{\partial a_J}{\partial v}+\frac{\partial}{\partial w} (ua_K)\right]$$

and

$$\frac{1}{u^2 \sin v}\left[\frac{\partial}{\partial u} (u^2 \sin v \, a_I)+\frac{\partial}{\partial v} (u \sin v \, a_J)+\frac{\partial}{\partial w} (ua_K)\right]$$

respectively.

The Laplacian of f has been defined by $\Delta f=\text{div grad} f$ and so by the combination of the formulae for gradient and divergence we have

$$\Delta f = \frac{1}{h_1 h_2 h_3}\left[\frac{\partial}{\partial u}\left(\frac{h_2 h_3}{h_1}\frac{\partial f}{\partial u}\right)+\frac{\partial}{\partial v}\left(\frac{h_3 h_1}{h_2}\frac{\partial f}{\partial v}\right)+\frac{\partial}{\partial w}\left(\frac{h_1 h_2}{h_3}\frac{\partial f}{\partial w}\right)\right]. \quad (64.2)$$

The corresponding results for cylindrical and spherical polar coordinates are

$$\frac{1}{u}\frac{\partial}{\partial u}\left(u\frac{\partial f}{\partial u}\right)+\frac{1}{u^2}\frac{\partial^2 f}{\partial v^2}+\frac{\partial^2 f}{\partial w^2}$$

and

$$\frac{1}{u^2}\frac{\partial}{\partial u}\left(u^2\frac{\partial f}{\partial u}\right)+\frac{1}{u^2\sin v}\frac{\partial}{\partial v}\left(\sin v\frac{\partial f}{\partial v}\right)+\frac{1}{u^2\sin^2 v}\frac{\partial^2 f}{\partial w^2}$$

respectively.

EXERCISES

1. If u, v, w are cylindrical coordinates, show that grad log u and grad v are solenoidal vectors in any region which does not contain the origin.

2. Obtain div $\mathbf{a}$ and Δf in the following coordinate systems: (i) parabolic cylindrical coordinates, (ii) paraboloidal coordinates, (iii) prolate ellipsoidal coordinates.

65   Curl

From curl $(f\mathbf{a})=f$ curl $\mathbf{a}+\text{grad} f\times\mathbf{a}$ we have

$$\text{curl}\,(a_I\mathbf{I}) = \text{curl}\,(a_I h_1\,\text{grad}\,u)$$
$$= a_I h_1\,\text{curl grad}\,u+\text{grad}\,(a_I h_1)\times\text{grad}\,u.$$

But curl grad $u=\mathbf{0}$ and so we have

$$\text{curl}\,(a_I\mathbf{I}) = \left\{\frac{1}{h_1}\frac{\partial}{\partial u}(a_I h_1)\mathbf{I}+\frac{1}{h_2}\frac{\partial}{\partial v}(a_I h_1)\mathbf{J}+\frac{1}{h_3}\frac{\partial}{\partial w}(a_I h_1)\mathbf{K}\right\}\times\frac{\mathbf{I}}{h_1}$$

$$= \frac{1}{h_3 h_1}\frac{\partial}{\partial w}(a_I h_1)\mathbf{J}-\frac{1}{h_1 h_2}\frac{\partial}{\partial v}(a_I h_1)\mathbf{K}.$$

Adding the corresponding results for curl $(a_J\mathbf{J})$ and curl $(a_K\mathbf{K})$ we have

$$\text{curl}\,\mathbf{a} = \frac{1}{h_2 h_3}\left\{\frac{\partial}{\partial v}(a_K h_3)-\frac{\partial}{\partial w}(a_J h_2)\right\}\mathbf{I}+\frac{1}{h_3 h_1}\left\{\frac{\partial}{\partial w}(a_I h_1)-\frac{\partial}{\partial u}(a_K h_3)\right\}\mathbf{J}$$

$$+\frac{1}{h_1 h_2}\left\{\frac{\partial}{\partial u}(a_J h_2)-\frac{\partial}{\partial v}(a_I h_1)\right\}\mathbf{K}. \qquad (65.1)$$

In particular, the corresponding results for cylindrical and spherical polar coordinates are

$$\frac{1}{u}\left[\frac{\partial a_K}{\partial v}-u\frac{\partial a_J}{\partial w}\right]\mathbf{I}+\left[\frac{\partial a_I}{\partial w}-\frac{\partial a_K}{\partial u}\right]\mathbf{J}+\frac{1}{u}\left[\frac{\partial}{\partial u}(ua_J)-\frac{\partial a_I}{\partial v}\right]\mathbf{K}$$

and

$$\frac{1}{u^2 \sin v} \left[u \frac{\partial}{\partial v} (\sin v \, a_K) - u \frac{\partial a_J}{\partial w} \right] \mathbf{I} + \frac{1}{u \sin v} \left[\frac{\partial a_I}{\partial w} - \sin v \frac{\partial}{\partial u} (u a_K) \right] \mathbf{J}$$

$$+ \frac{1}{u} \left[\frac{\partial}{\partial u} (u a_J) - \frac{\partial a_I}{\partial v} \right] \mathbf{K}.$$

EXERCISE

1. Obtain curl $\mathbf{a}$ in the following coordinate systems: (i) parabolic cylindrical coordinates, (ii) paraboloidal coordinates, (iii) prolate ellipsoidal coordinates.

66   Curl of the Curl of a Vector

With reference to a fundamental basis $\mathbf{i}, \mathbf{j}$ and $\mathbf{k}$ we have

$$\text{curl } \mathbf{a} = \left(\frac{\partial a_k}{\partial v} - \frac{\partial a_j}{\partial w} \right) \mathbf{i} + \left(\frac{\partial a_i}{\partial w} - \frac{\partial a_k}{\partial u} \right) \mathbf{j} + \left(\frac{\partial a_j}{\partial u} - \frac{\partial a_i}{\partial v} \right) \mathbf{k},$$

and so the coefficient of $\mathbf{i}$ in curl curl $\mathbf{a}$ is

$$\frac{\partial}{\partial v} \left(\frac{\partial a_j}{\partial u} - \frac{\partial a_i}{\partial v} \right) - \frac{\partial}{\partial w} \left(\frac{\partial a_i}{\partial w} - \frac{\partial a_k}{\partial u} \right)$$

$$= - \left(\frac{\partial^2 a_i}{\partial u^2} + \frac{\partial^2 a_i}{\partial v^2} + \frac{\partial^2 a_i}{\partial w^2} \right) + \frac{\partial}{\partial u} \left(\frac{\partial a_i}{\partial u} + \frac{\partial a_j}{\partial v} + \frac{\partial a_k}{\partial w} \right).$$

Let us define the Laplacian operating on a vector by

$$\Delta \mathbf{a} = \Delta a_i \mathbf{i} + \Delta a_j \mathbf{j} + \Delta a_k \mathbf{k}.$$

Then we have

$$\text{curl curl } \mathbf{a} = \text{grad div } \mathbf{a} - \Delta \mathbf{a}. \tag{66.1}$$

It is important to note that this relation has only been proved for a fundamental basis. Some authors *define* $\Delta \mathbf{a}$ in an orthogonal curvilinear coordinate system by this relation. The reader is referred to Section 76 for a full treatment of curl curl $\mathbf{a}$. There we show that this relation is always valid for one particular basis, called the *natural basis*.

MISCELLANEOUS EXERCISES

1. Show that

$$\frac{\partial \mathbf{I}}{\partial u} = -\frac{1}{h_2}\frac{\partial h_1}{\partial v}\mathbf{J} - \frac{1}{h_3}\frac{\partial h_1}{\partial w}\mathbf{K}, \quad \frac{\partial \mathbf{I}}{\partial v} = \frac{1}{h_1}\frac{\partial h_2}{\partial u}\mathbf{J}, \quad \frac{\partial \mathbf{I}}{\partial w} = \frac{1}{h_1}\frac{\partial h_3}{\partial u}\mathbf{K},$$

$$\frac{\partial \mathbf{J}}{\partial u} = \frac{1}{h_2}\frac{\partial h_1}{\partial v}\mathbf{J}, \quad \frac{\partial \mathbf{J}}{\partial v} = -\frac{1}{h_1}\frac{\partial h_2}{\partial u}\mathbf{I} - \frac{1}{h_3}\frac{\partial h_2}{\partial w}\mathbf{K}, \quad \frac{\partial \mathbf{J}}{\partial w} = \frac{1}{h_2}\frac{\partial h_3}{\partial v}\mathbf{K},$$

$$\frac{\partial \mathbf{K}}{\partial u} = \frac{1}{h_3}\frac{\partial h_1}{\partial w}\mathbf{I}, \quad \frac{\partial \mathbf{K}}{\partial v} = \frac{1}{h_3}\frac{\partial h_2}{\partial w}\mathbf{J}, \quad \frac{\partial \mathbf{K}}{\partial w} = -\frac{1}{h_1}\frac{\partial h_3}{\partial u}\mathbf{I} - \frac{1}{h_2}\frac{\partial h_3}{\partial v}\mathbf{J}.$$

$\bigg($Hint: The derivatives are linear combinations of the basis vectors. Use relations of the type

$$\mathbf{I}.\frac{\partial \mathbf{I}}{\partial u} = 0, \ \mathbf{I}.\frac{\partial \mathbf{J}}{\partial u} = -\mathbf{J}.\frac{\partial \mathbf{I}}{\partial u} \ \text{and} \ \frac{\partial}{\partial w}(h_2\mathbf{J}) = \frac{\partial}{\partial v}(h_3\mathbf{K}) = \frac{\partial^2 \mathbf{r}}{\partial v\,\partial w}.\bigg)$$

2. If $\mathbf{I}$, $\mathbf{J}$ and $\mathbf{K}$ are the basis vectors for a spherical polar coordinate system, show that

$$\text{curl curl }\mathbf{I} = 0, \quad \text{curl curl }\mathbf{J} = \frac{\cot v}{u^2}\mathbf{I}, \quad \text{curl curl }\mathbf{K} = \frac{\text{cosec}^2 v}{u^2}\mathbf{K},$$

$$\text{grad div }\mathbf{I} = -\frac{2}{u^2}\mathbf{I}, \quad \text{grad div }\mathbf{J} = -\frac{\cot v}{u^2}\mathbf{I} - \frac{\text{cosec}^2 v}{u^2}\mathbf{J},$$

$$\text{grad div }\mathbf{K} = 0.$$

3. In an orthogonal curvilinear coordinate system for which $h_1 = 1$, h_2 is a function of u and h_3 is a function of u and v, show that

$$\Delta\mathbf{I} = \frac{1}{h_1 h_2 h_3}\bigg[\frac{\partial}{\partial u}\bigg(\frac{h_2 h_3}{h_1}\frac{\partial \mathbf{I}}{\partial u}\bigg) + \frac{\partial}{\partial v}\bigg(\frac{h_3 h_1}{h_2}\frac{\partial \mathbf{I}}{\partial v}\bigg) + \frac{\partial}{\partial w}\bigg(\frac{h_1 h_2}{h_3}\frac{\partial \mathbf{I}}{\partial w}\bigg)\bigg].$$

CHAPTER 12

Contravariance and Covariance

67 Contravariant Components

Consider the basis formed at each point by the three independent vector fields e_1, e_2 and e_3. These vectors are not in general unit vectors, nor are they mutually orthogonal. We may write

$$\mathbf{a} = a^1\mathbf{e}_1 + a^2\mathbf{e}_2 + a^3\mathbf{e}_3$$

and then refer to a^1, a^2, a^3 as the **contravariant components** of $\mathbf{a}$ with respect to the basis $\mathbf{e}_\alpha$. For brevity, the convention is made that all Greek indices have the range 1, 2, 3.

Further, we introduce the **Einstein summation convention** that a repeated index implies summation over the range of values 1, 2 and 3. That is, we may write

$$\mathbf{a} = a^\alpha \mathbf{e}_\alpha.$$

Let the contravariant components of $\mathbf{a}$ with respect to a second basis $\mathbf{e}'_\alpha$ be a'^α. That is,

$$\mathbf{a} = a'^\alpha \mathbf{e}'_\alpha.$$

Both sets of vector fields $\mathbf{e}_\alpha$ and $\mathbf{e}'_\alpha$ form bases and so we may express each vector of either basis linearly in terms of the vectors of the other basis. Accordingly,

$$\mathbf{e}'_\alpha = p^\beta_\alpha \mathbf{e}_\beta \quad \text{and} \quad \mathbf{e}_\alpha = q^\beta_\alpha \mathbf{e}'_\beta, \tag{67.1}$$

where p^β_α and q^β_α each represent nine quantities which are not in general constants.

The *repeated* index β, called a **dummy index**, in the above equation can be changed to γ whilst the *free* index α can be changed to β. As a result we may rewrite the equations in the forms

$$\mathbf{e}'_\beta = p^\gamma_\beta \mathbf{e}_\gamma \quad \text{and} \quad \mathbf{e}_\beta = q^\gamma_\beta \mathbf{e}'_\gamma.$$

Substitute in the previous equations to obtain

$$\mathbf{e}'_\alpha = p^\beta_\alpha q^\gamma_\beta \mathbf{e}'_\gamma \quad \text{and} \quad \mathbf{e}_\alpha = p^\gamma_\beta q^\beta_\alpha \mathbf{e}_\gamma,$$

where the two sets of repeated indices imply double summations. Introduce the **Kronecker delta** by

$$\delta^\gamma_\alpha = \begin{cases} 1 & \text{if } \gamma = \alpha, \\ 0 & \text{if } \gamma \neq \alpha, \end{cases}$$

and we deduce† that

$$p^\beta_\alpha q^\gamma_\beta = p^\gamma_\beta q^\beta_\alpha = \delta^\gamma_\alpha.$$

Further, we have

$$\mathbf{a} = a^\alpha \mathbf{e}_\alpha = a'^\alpha \mathbf{e}'_\alpha,$$

and so

$$a^\alpha q^\beta_\alpha \mathbf{e}'_\beta = a'^\beta \mathbf{e}'_\beta \quad \text{and} \quad a^\beta \mathbf{e}_\beta = a'^\alpha p^\beta_\alpha \mathbf{e}_\beta.$$

The vectors $\mathbf{e}_\beta$ and $\mathbf{e}'_\beta$ form bases and so no linear combination of them can vanish. Accordingly, we have

$$a'^\beta = q^\beta_\alpha a^\alpha \quad \text{and} \quad a^\beta = p^\beta_\alpha a'^\alpha. \tag{67.2}$$

68 Covariant Components

Let the vector fields $\mathbf{e}^1$, $\mathbf{e}^2$ and $\mathbf{e}^3$ be reciprocal to $\mathbf{e}_1$, $\mathbf{e}_2$ and $\mathbf{e}_3$. Then the conditions of (13.1) can be written

$$\mathbf{e}_\alpha . \mathbf{e}^\beta = \delta^\beta_\alpha.$$

If $\mathbf{e}'^\alpha$ form the basis reciprocal to $\mathbf{e}'_\alpha$ we have

$$\mathbf{e}'_\alpha . \mathbf{e}'^\beta = \delta^\beta_\alpha.$$

We may write

$$\mathbf{a} = a_1 \mathbf{e}^1 + a_2 \mathbf{e}^2 + a_3 \mathbf{e}^3 = a_\alpha \mathbf{e}^\alpha.$$

The quantities a_1, a_2, a_3 are called the **covariant components** of $\mathbf{a}$ with respect to the basis $\mathbf{e}_\alpha$. Note carefully that a_1, a_2, a_3 are *contravariant* components with respect to the reciprocal basis $\mathbf{e}^\alpha$.

From $\mathbf{a} = a_\alpha \mathbf{e}^\alpha = a'_\alpha \mathbf{e}'^\alpha$, we have in virtue of equation (67.1) that

$$a_\alpha \mathbf{e}^\alpha . \mathbf{e}_\beta = a'_\alpha \mathbf{e}'^\alpha . \mathbf{e}_\beta = a'_\alpha \mathbf{e}'^\alpha . q^\gamma_\beta \mathbf{e}'_\gamma$$

and so

$$a_\alpha \delta^\alpha_\beta = a'_\alpha q^\gamma_\beta \delta^\alpha_\gamma,$$

from which by summation we have

$$a_\beta = q^\gamma_\beta a'_\gamma. \tag{68.1}$$

† The reader familiar with matrices will recognize that $[q^\beta_\alpha]$ is the matrix inverse to $[p^\beta_\alpha]$.

Similarly, we obtain

$$a'_\beta = p^\gamma_\beta a_\gamma.$$ (68.2)

Further, we have in virtue of equation (67.2) that

$$\mathbf{a} = a_\gamma \mathbf{e}^\gamma = a'_\beta \mathbf{e}'^\beta = p^\gamma_\beta a_\gamma \mathbf{e}'^\beta$$

and so

$$a_\gamma(\mathbf{e}^\gamma - p^\gamma_\beta \mathbf{e}'^\beta) = \mathbf{0}.$$

The components a_γ are arbitrary. We may in turn select one component to be unity and the others to be zero and we obtain

$$\mathbf{e}^\gamma = p^\gamma_\beta \mathbf{e}'^\beta.$$ (68.3)

Similarly, we obtain

$$\mathbf{e}'^\gamma = q^\gamma_\beta \mathbf{e}^\beta.$$ (68.4)

EXERCISES

1. Show that $a'_\beta = p^\gamma_\beta a_\gamma$.
2. Show that $\mathbf{e}'^\gamma = q^\gamma_\beta \mathbf{e}^\beta$.

69 Fundamental Tensors

We define $g_{\alpha\beta} = g_{\beta\alpha}$, called the **covariant fundamental tensor,** by

$$g_{\alpha\beta} = \mathbf{e}_\alpha \cdot \mathbf{e}_\beta = g_{\beta\alpha}.$$

From

$$\mathbf{a} = a^\alpha \mathbf{e}_\alpha = a_\alpha \mathbf{e}^\alpha$$

we have

$$a^\alpha \mathbf{e}_\alpha \cdot \mathbf{e}_\beta = a_\alpha \mathbf{e}^\alpha \cdot \mathbf{e}_\beta = a_\alpha \delta^\alpha_\beta = a_\beta$$

and so

$$a_\beta = g_{\alpha\beta} a^\alpha.$$ (69.1)

Further, define $g^{\alpha\beta} = g^{\beta\alpha}$, called the **contravariant fundamental tensor,** by

$$g^{\alpha\beta} = \mathbf{e}^\alpha \cdot \mathbf{e}^\beta = g^{\beta\alpha}.$$

Then we have

$$a^\alpha \mathbf{e}_\alpha \cdot \mathbf{e}^\beta = a_\alpha \mathbf{e}^\alpha \cdot \mathbf{e}^\beta,$$

from which we obtain

$$a^\beta = g^{\alpha\beta} a_\alpha.$$ (69.2)

Again, using equation (69.1) we have

$$a^\alpha \mathbf{e}_\alpha = a_\beta \mathbf{e}^\beta = g_{\alpha\beta} a^\alpha \mathbf{e}^\beta$$

and so

$$a^\alpha(\mathbf{e}_\alpha - g_{\alpha\beta} \mathbf{e}^\beta) = \mathbf{0}.$$

Since the components a^α are arbitrary, we have as in the preceding section that

$$\mathbf{e}_\alpha = g_{\alpha\beta}\mathbf{e}^\beta. \tag{69.3}$$

In a similar way, we obtain

$$\mathbf{e}^\alpha = g^{\alpha\beta}\mathbf{e}_\beta. \tag{69.4}$$

Hence we have

$$\mathbf{e}^\alpha = g^{\alpha\beta}g_{\beta\gamma}\mathbf{e}^\gamma$$

and so†

$$g^{\alpha\beta}g_{\beta\gamma} = \delta^\alpha_\gamma. \tag{69.5}$$

EXERCISES

1. Show that $\mathbf{e}^\alpha = g^{\alpha\beta}\mathbf{e}_\beta$.
2. If $\mathbf{a}$ and $\mathbf{b}$ are vectors, show with the usual notation that

$$\mathbf{a}.\mathbf{b} = a^\alpha b_\alpha = a_\alpha b^\alpha = g^{\alpha\beta}a_\alpha b_\beta = g_{\alpha\beta}a^\alpha b^\beta.$$

70   Natural Basis

Consider the coordinate systems u^α and u'^α and let $\mathbf{r}$ denote the vector position relative to the origin O of the u^α system and $\mathbf{r}+\mathbf{c}$ denote the vector position relative to the origin O' of the u'^α system, where $\mathbf{c}$ is the constant vector $\overrightarrow{O'O}$. We choose as the **natural bases** the vectors $\mathbf{e}_\alpha$ and $\mathbf{e}'_\alpha$ given by

$$\mathbf{e}_\alpha = \frac{\partial \mathbf{r}}{\partial u^\alpha} \quad \text{and} \quad \mathbf{e}'_\alpha = \frac{\partial(\mathbf{r}+\mathbf{c})}{\partial u'^\alpha} = \frac{\partial \mathbf{r}}{\partial u'^\alpha}.$$

The chain rule of partial differentiation states that

$$\frac{\partial \mathbf{r}}{\partial u'^\alpha} = \frac{\partial \mathbf{r}}{\partial u^\beta}\frac{\partial u^\beta}{\partial u'^\alpha} \quad \text{and} \quad \frac{\partial \mathbf{r}}{\partial u^\alpha} = \frac{\partial \mathbf{r}}{\partial u'^\beta}\frac{\partial u'^\beta}{\partial u^\alpha}.$$

Hence we have

$$\mathbf{e}'_\alpha = \frac{\partial u^\beta}{\partial u'^\alpha}\mathbf{e}_\beta \quad \text{and} \quad \mathbf{e}_\alpha = \frac{\partial u'^\beta}{\partial u^\alpha}\mathbf{e}'_\beta.$$

Accordingly the p^β_α and q^β_α defined in Section 67 are given by

$$p^\beta_\alpha = \frac{\partial u^\beta}{\partial u'^\alpha} \quad \text{and} \quad q^\beta_\alpha = \frac{\partial u'^\beta}{\partial u^\alpha}$$

† That is, the matrix $[g^{\alpha\beta}]$ is the inverse of the matrix $[g_{\alpha\beta}]$.

and so, using (67.2), (68.1) and (68.2), the contravariant and covariant components of the vector **a** transform by

$$\left.\begin{array}{ll} a^\beta = \dfrac{\partial u^\beta}{\partial u'^\alpha} a'^\alpha, & a'^\beta = \dfrac{\partial u'^\beta}{\partial u^\alpha} a^\alpha, \\[12pt] a_\beta = \dfrac{\partial u'^\alpha}{\partial u^\beta} a'_\alpha, & a'_\beta = \dfrac{\partial u^\alpha}{\partial u'^\beta} a_\alpha. \end{array}\right\} \tag{70.1}$$

The transformation laws with respect to the natural bases have a simple structure and provide the starting point in the development of the tensor calculus.

71 Physical Components of a Vector

We have defined the contravariant and covariant components of a vector with respect to any given basis. But the component as defined in Chapter 1, for emphasis now called the **physical component**, of a vector **a** along the direction given by the *unit* vector **1** is **a**.**1**.

We have $\mathbf{e}_\alpha.\mathbf{e}_\beta = g_{\alpha\beta}$ and $\mathbf{e}^\alpha.\mathbf{e}^\beta = g^{\alpha\beta}$ and so $|\mathbf{e}_\alpha|^2 = g_{\alpha\alpha}$ and $|\mathbf{e}^\alpha|^2 = g^{\alpha\alpha}$, where there is *no* summation over the repeated index α. That is, the unit vectors in the directions $\mathbf{e}_\alpha$ and $\mathbf{e}^\alpha$ are respectively $\mathbf{e}_\alpha/\sqrt{g_{\alpha\alpha}}$ and $\mathbf{e}^\alpha/\sqrt{g^{\alpha\alpha}}$, (no summation). Hence the physical components of **a** along the directions $\mathbf{e}_\alpha$ and $\mathbf{e}^\alpha$ are

$$\mathbf{a}.\mathbf{e}_\alpha/\sqrt{g_{\alpha\alpha}} = a_\beta\mathbf{e}^\beta.\mathbf{e}_\alpha/\sqrt{g_{\alpha\alpha}} = a_\beta\delta^\beta_\alpha/\sqrt{g_{\alpha\alpha}} = a_\alpha/\sqrt{g_{\alpha\alpha}}$$

and

$$\mathbf{a}.\mathbf{e}^\alpha/\sqrt{g^{\alpha\alpha}} = a^\beta\mathbf{e}_\beta.\mathbf{e}^\alpha/\sqrt{g^{\alpha\alpha}} = a^\beta\delta^\alpha_\beta/\sqrt{g^{\alpha\alpha}} = a^\alpha/\sqrt{g^{\alpha\alpha}}.$$

When the basis vectors consist of three mutually orthogonal unit vectors we have $g_{\alpha\beta} = \delta^\alpha_\beta$ and consequently $\mathbf{e}_\alpha = \mathbf{e}^\alpha$. That is, the basis is self-reciprocal. We see in this case that the contravariant, covariant and physical components are identical.

Consider the vector grad f whose components referred to a rectangular Cartesian coordinate system x^α are $\partial f/\partial x^\alpha$. On transformation to the u^α coordinate system, the covariant components with respect to the natural basis are given in virtue of (70.1) by

$$\frac{\partial f}{\partial x^\alpha}\frac{\partial x^\alpha}{\partial u^\beta} = \frac{\partial f}{\partial u^\beta}.$$

If the u^α form an orthogonal curvilinear coordinate system, we have $g_{\alpha\alpha} = h_\alpha^2$ (no summation) and so the physical components of the gradient are $\dfrac{1}{h_\alpha}\dfrac{\partial f}{\partial u^\alpha}$ (no summation) as already obtained in Section 63.

72 Derivatives of Natural Basis Vectors

The natural basis vectors have been defined by $\mathbf{e}_\alpha = \partial\mathbf{r}/\partial u^\alpha$ and so it follows that

$$\frac{\partial\mathbf{e}_\alpha}{\partial u^\beta} = \frac{\partial\mathbf{e}_\beta}{\partial u^\alpha}.$$

Further, differentiation of the relation $\mathbf{e}_\alpha.\mathbf{e}_\beta = g_{\alpha\beta}$ with respect to u^γ yields

$$\frac{\partial\mathbf{e}_\alpha}{\partial u^\gamma}.\mathbf{e}_\beta + \mathbf{e}_\alpha.\frac{\partial\mathbf{e}_\beta}{\partial u^\gamma} = \frac{\partial g_{\alpha\beta}}{\partial u^\gamma}.$$

Note carefully that $\partial\mathbf{e}_\alpha/\partial u^\gamma$ represents nine vectors, each of which can be expressed in terms of the basis vectors themselves. Accordingly, we may write

$$\frac{\partial\mathbf{e}_\alpha}{\partial u^\beta} = \lambda^\rho_{\alpha\beta}\mathbf{e}_\rho,$$

where $\lambda^\rho_{\alpha\beta}$ represents the 27 coefficients involved. Substitution in the previous equation yields

$$\lambda^\rho_{\alpha\gamma}\mathbf{e}_\rho.\mathbf{e}_\beta + \mathbf{e}_\alpha.\lambda^\rho_{\beta\gamma}\mathbf{e}_\rho = \frac{\partial g_{\alpha\beta}}{\partial u^\gamma}.$$

That is, in virtue of the definitions in Section 69,

$$g_{\rho\beta}\lambda^\rho_{\alpha\gamma} + g_{\alpha\rho}\lambda^\rho_{\beta\gamma} = \frac{\partial g_{\alpha\beta}}{\partial u^\gamma}.$$

Permuting the indices α, β and γ cyclically we obtain

$$g_{\rho\gamma}\lambda^\rho_{\beta\alpha} + g_{\beta\rho}\lambda^\rho_{\gamma\alpha} = \frac{\partial g_{\beta\gamma}}{\partial u^\alpha}$$

and

$$g_{\rho\alpha}\lambda^\rho_{\gamma\beta} + g_{\gamma\rho}\lambda^\rho_{\alpha\beta} = \frac{\partial g_{\gamma\alpha}}{\partial u^\beta}.$$

We introduce the **Christoffel symbols** $[\alpha\beta, \gamma]$ and $\left\{{\delta \atop \alpha\beta}\right\}$ defined by

$$[\alpha\beta, \gamma] = \tfrac{1}{2}\left(\frac{\partial g_{\beta\gamma}}{\partial u^\alpha} + \frac{\partial g_{\alpha\gamma}}{\partial u^\beta} - \frac{\partial g_{\alpha\beta}}{\partial u^\gamma}\right) = [\beta\alpha, \gamma]$$

and

$$\left\{{\delta \atop \alpha\beta}\right\} = g^{\gamma\delta}[\alpha\beta, \gamma] = \left\{{\delta \atop \beta\alpha}\right\}.$$

In virtue of $\dfrac{\partial\mathbf{e}_\alpha}{\partial u^\beta} = \dfrac{\partial\mathbf{e}_\beta}{\partial u^\alpha}$ we have $\lambda^\rho_{\alpha\beta} = \lambda^\rho_{\beta\alpha}$ and so a simple calculation gives

$$g_{\rho\gamma}\lambda^{\rho}_{\alpha\beta} = [\alpha\beta, \gamma].$$

Hence we have

$$\lambda^{\sigma}_{\alpha\beta} = \delta^{\sigma}_{\rho}\lambda^{\rho}_{\alpha\beta} = g^{\gamma\sigma}g_{\gamma\rho}\lambda^{\rho}_{\alpha\beta} = g^{\gamma\sigma}[\alpha\beta, \gamma] = \left\{\begin{matrix}\sigma\\\alpha\beta\end{matrix}\right\},$$

and so the derivatives of the basis vectors are given by

$$\frac{\partial \mathbf{e}_{\alpha}}{\partial u^{\beta}} = \left\{\begin{matrix}\rho\\\alpha\beta\end{matrix}\right\} \mathbf{e}_{\rho}. \qquad (72.1)$$

To obtain the corresponding derivatives of the $\mathbf{e}^{\alpha}$, we differentiate the relation $\mathbf{e}_{\alpha}.\mathbf{e}^{\beta} = \delta^{\beta}_{\alpha}$ with respect to u^{γ} to yield

$$\mathbf{e}_{\alpha}.\frac{\partial \mathbf{e}^{\beta}}{\partial u^{\gamma}} + \frac{\partial \mathbf{e}_{\alpha}}{\partial u^{\gamma}}.\mathbf{e}^{\beta} = 0.$$

Let $\dfrac{\partial \mathbf{e}^{\beta}}{\partial u^{\gamma}} = \mu^{\beta}_{\gamma\rho}\mathbf{e}^{\rho}$ and we have by substitution that

$$\mathbf{e}_{\alpha}.\mu^{\beta}_{\gamma\rho}\mathbf{e}^{\rho} + \left\{\begin{matrix}\rho\\\alpha\gamma\end{matrix}\right\} \mathbf{e}_{\rho}.\mathbf{e}^{\beta} = 0.$$

That is,

$$\delta^{\rho}_{\alpha}\mu^{\beta}_{\gamma\rho} + \delta^{\beta}_{\rho}\left\{\begin{matrix}\rho\\\alpha\gamma\end{matrix}\right\} = 0$$

from which

$$\mu^{\beta}_{\gamma\alpha} = -\left\{\begin{matrix}\beta\\\alpha\gamma\end{matrix}\right\}.$$

Accordingly the required relations are

$$\frac{\partial \mathbf{e}^{\alpha}}{\partial u^{\beta}} = -\left\{\begin{matrix}\alpha\\\beta\rho\end{matrix}\right\} \mathbf{e}^{\rho}. \qquad (72.2)$$

73 Derivatives of Vectors

Consider the vector $\mathbf{a} = a^{\alpha}\mathbf{e}_{\alpha}$. On differentiation we have

$$\frac{\partial \mathbf{a}}{\partial u^{\beta}} = \frac{\partial a^{\alpha}}{\partial u^{\beta}}\mathbf{e}_{\alpha} + a^{\alpha}\frac{\partial \mathbf{e}_{\alpha}}{\partial u^{\beta}}$$

$$= \frac{\partial a^{\rho}}{\partial u^{\beta}}\mathbf{e}_{\rho} + a^{\alpha}\left\{\begin{matrix}\rho\\\alpha\beta\end{matrix}\right\}\mathbf{e}_{\rho}$$

$$= a^{\rho}_{,\beta}\mathbf{e}_{\rho},$$

where we have written

$$a^{\rho}_{,\beta} = \frac{\partial a^{\rho}}{\partial u^{\beta}} + \left\{ \begin{matrix} \rho \\ \alpha\beta \end{matrix} \right\} a^{\alpha}.$$

The expression $a^{\rho}_{,\beta}$ is called the **covariant derivative** of a^{ρ} with respect to u^{β}.

Similarly from $\mathbf{a} = a_{\alpha}\mathbf{e}^{\alpha}$ we have

$$\frac{\partial \mathbf{a}}{\partial u^{\beta}} = \frac{\partial a_{\alpha}}{\partial u^{\beta}} \mathbf{e}^{\alpha} + a_{\alpha} \frac{\partial \mathbf{e}^{\alpha}}{\partial u^{\beta}}$$

$$= \frac{\partial a_{\rho}}{\partial u^{\beta}} \mathbf{e}^{\rho} - a_{\alpha} \left\{ \begin{matrix} \alpha \\ \beta\rho \end{matrix} \right\} \mathbf{e}^{\rho}$$

$$= a_{\rho,\beta}\mathbf{e}^{\rho},$$

where we have written

$$a_{\rho,\beta} = \frac{\partial a_{\rho}}{\partial u^{\beta}} - \left\{ \begin{matrix} \alpha \\ \beta\rho \end{matrix} \right\} a_{\alpha}.$$

The expression $a_{\rho,\beta}$ is called the **covariant derivative** of a_{ρ} with respect to u^{β}.

EXERCISES

1. If the basis vectors are constant, show that covariant differentiation is partial differentiation.

2. By considering $\dfrac{\partial^{2}\mathbf{a}}{\partial u^{\alpha} \, \partial u^{\beta}} = \dfrac{\partial^{2}\mathbf{a}}{\partial u^{\beta} \, \partial u^{\alpha}}$, show that

$$\frac{\partial}{\partial u^{\gamma}} \left\{ \begin{matrix} \alpha \\ \beta\rho \end{matrix} \right\} - \frac{\partial}{\partial u^{\beta}} \left\{ \begin{matrix} \alpha \\ \gamma\rho \end{matrix} \right\} + \left\{ \begin{matrix} \sigma \\ \beta\rho \end{matrix} \right\} \left\{ \begin{matrix} \alpha \\ \sigma\gamma \end{matrix} \right\} - \left\{ \begin{matrix} \sigma \\ \gamma\rho \end{matrix} \right\} \left\{ \begin{matrix} \alpha \\ \sigma\beta \end{matrix} \right\} = 0.$$

74 Gradient

In Section 71, we saw that the *covariant* components of $\operatorname{grad} f$ referred to the natural basis $\mathbf{e}_{\alpha}$ are $\partial f / \partial u^{\alpha}$. Accordingly, we have

$$\operatorname{grad} f = \frac{\partial f}{\partial u^{\alpha}} \mathbf{e}^{\alpha}. \qquad (74.1)$$

Hence

$$\operatorname{grad} u^{\alpha} = \mathbf{e}^{\alpha} \quad \text{and} \quad \operatorname{curl} \mathbf{e}^{\alpha} = \operatorname{curl} \operatorname{grad} u^{\alpha} = \mathbf{0}. \qquad (74.2)$$

Let us write $\lambda = [\mathbf{e}^{1}\mathbf{e}^{2}\mathbf{e}^{3}]$ and we have

$$\frac{\partial \lambda}{\partial u^{\alpha}} = \left[\frac{\partial \mathbf{e}^{1}}{\partial u^{\alpha}} \mathbf{e}^{2}\mathbf{e}^{3} \right] + \left[\mathbf{e}^{1} \frac{\partial \mathbf{e}^{2}}{\partial u^{\alpha}} \mathbf{e}^{3} \right] + \left[\mathbf{e}^{1}\mathbf{e}^{2} \frac{\partial \mathbf{e}^{3}}{\partial u^{\alpha}} \right]$$

$$= -\left\{ \begin{matrix} 1 \\ \alpha\beta \end{matrix} \right\} \left[\mathbf{e}^{\beta}\mathbf{e}^{2}\mathbf{e}^{3} \right] - \left\{ \begin{matrix} 2 \\ \alpha\beta \end{matrix} \right\} \left[\mathbf{e}^{1}\mathbf{e}^{\beta}\mathbf{e}^{3} \right] - \left\{ \begin{matrix} 3 \\ \alpha\beta \end{matrix} \right\} \left[\mathbf{e}^{1}\mathbf{e}^{2}\mathbf{e}^{\beta} \right]$$

$$= -\left[\left\{ \begin{matrix} 1 \\ \alpha1 \end{matrix} \right\} + \left\{ \begin{matrix} 2 \\ \alpha2 \end{matrix} \right\} + \left\{ \begin{matrix} 3 \\ \alpha3 \end{matrix} \right\} \right] \left[\mathbf{e}^{1}\mathbf{e}^{2}\mathbf{e}^{3} \right] = -\left\{ \begin{matrix} \beta \\ \alpha\beta \end{matrix} \right\} \lambda.$$

Consequently, we obtain

$$\text{grad } \lambda = \frac{\partial \lambda}{\partial u^\alpha} \mathbf{e}^\alpha = -\begin{Bmatrix} \beta \\ \alpha\beta \end{Bmatrix} \lambda \mathbf{e}^\alpha. \qquad (74.3)$$

75 Divergence

From equation (46.1) we have div $(\mathbf{e}^\alpha \times \mathbf{e}^\beta) = \mathbf{e}^\beta . \text{curl } \mathbf{e}^\alpha - \mathbf{e}^\alpha . \text{curl } \mathbf{e}^\beta$. Further, equation (74.2) states that curl $\mathbf{e}^\alpha = \mathbf{0}$ and equations (13.3) take the form $\lambda \mathbf{e}_1 = \mathbf{e}^2 \times \mathbf{e}^3$, etc. Accordingly we derive div $(\lambda \mathbf{e}_\alpha) = 0$ from which in virtue of (43.1) we have

$$\lambda \text{ div } \mathbf{e}_\alpha + \text{grad } \lambda . \mathbf{e}_\alpha = 0.$$

On application of (74.3) we deduce that

$$\text{div } \mathbf{e}_\alpha = \begin{Bmatrix} \beta \\ \gamma\beta \end{Bmatrix} \mathbf{e}^\gamma . \mathbf{e}_\alpha = \begin{Bmatrix} \beta \\ \gamma\beta \end{Bmatrix} \delta^\gamma_\alpha = \begin{Bmatrix} \beta \\ \alpha\beta \end{Bmatrix}.$$

Using equation (69.4) the divergence of the reciprocal vectors may be calculated from

$$\text{div } \mathbf{e}^\alpha = \text{div } (\mathbf{e}^\alpha . \mathbf{e}^\beta \mathbf{e}_\beta)$$
$$= \mathbf{e}^\alpha . \mathbf{e}^\beta \text{ div } \mathbf{e}_\beta + \text{grad } (\mathbf{e}^\alpha . \mathbf{e}^\beta) . \mathbf{e}_\beta$$
$$= g^{\alpha\beta} \begin{Bmatrix} \gamma \\ \beta\gamma \end{Bmatrix} + \frac{\partial}{\partial u^\gamma} (\mathbf{e}^\alpha . \mathbf{e}^\beta) \mathbf{e}^\gamma . \mathbf{e}_\beta.$$

Use of $\mathbf{e}^\gamma . \mathbf{e}_\beta = \delta^\gamma_\beta$, $\frac{\partial \mathbf{e}^\alpha}{\partial u^\gamma} = -\begin{Bmatrix} \alpha \\ \gamma\sigma \end{Bmatrix} \mathbf{e}^\sigma$ and appropriate changes of dummy indices yields

$$\text{div } \mathbf{e}^\alpha = -g^{\beta\gamma} \begin{Bmatrix} \alpha \\ \beta\gamma \end{Bmatrix}.$$

Accordingly, we have

$$\text{div } \mathbf{a} = \text{div } (a^\alpha \mathbf{e}_\alpha) \qquad\qquad = \text{div } (a_\alpha \mathbf{e}^\alpha)$$
$$= a^\alpha \text{ div } \mathbf{e}_\alpha + \text{grad } a^\alpha . \mathbf{e}_\alpha \quad = a_\alpha \text{ div } \mathbf{e}^\alpha + \text{grad } a_\alpha . \mathbf{e}^\alpha$$
$$= a^\alpha \begin{Bmatrix} \beta \\ \alpha\beta \end{Bmatrix} + \frac{\partial a^\alpha}{\partial u^\beta} \mathbf{e}^\beta . \mathbf{e}_\alpha \quad = -a_\alpha g^{\beta\gamma} \begin{Bmatrix} \alpha \\ \beta\gamma \end{Bmatrix} + \frac{\partial a_\alpha}{\partial u^\beta} \mathbf{e}^\beta . \mathbf{e}^\alpha$$
$$= \frac{\partial a^\alpha}{\partial u^\beta} \delta^\beta_\alpha + \begin{Bmatrix} \beta \\ \alpha\beta \end{Bmatrix} a^\alpha \quad = g^{\alpha\beta} \left(\frac{\partial a_\alpha}{\partial u^\beta} - \begin{Bmatrix} \gamma \\ \alpha\beta \end{Bmatrix} a_\gamma \right)$$
$$= a^\alpha_{,\alpha} \qquad\qquad\qquad = a_{\alpha,\beta} \mathbf{e}^\alpha . \mathbf{e}^\beta.$$

We deduce that

$$\text{grad div } \mathbf{a} = \frac{\partial}{\partial u^\gamma}(a_{\alpha,\beta}\, \mathbf{e}^\alpha . \mathbf{e}^\beta)\mathbf{e}^\gamma$$

$$= \frac{\partial a_{\alpha,\beta}}{\partial u^\gamma}\, \mathbf{e}^\alpha . \mathbf{e}^\beta\, \mathbf{e}^\gamma - a_{\alpha,\beta}\begin{Bmatrix}\alpha\\\gamma\sigma\end{Bmatrix}\mathbf{e}^\sigma . \mathbf{e}^\beta\, \mathbf{e}^\gamma - a_{\alpha,\beta}\mathbf{e}^\alpha . \mathbf{e}^\sigma\begin{Bmatrix}\beta\\\gamma\sigma\end{Bmatrix}\mathbf{e}^\gamma$$

$$= \left[\frac{\partial a_{\alpha,\beta}}{\partial u^\gamma} - \begin{Bmatrix}\sigma\\\gamma\alpha\end{Bmatrix}a_{\sigma,\beta} - \begin{Bmatrix}\sigma\\\beta\gamma\end{Bmatrix}a_{\alpha,\sigma}\right]\mathbf{e}^\alpha . \mathbf{e}^\beta\, \mathbf{e}^\gamma$$

$$= a_{\alpha,\beta\gamma}\, \mathbf{e}^\alpha . \mathbf{e}^\beta\, \mathbf{e}^\gamma,$$

where we define $a_{\alpha,\beta\gamma}$ by the expression in the square brackets in the line above.

The **Laplacian** $\varDelta\mathbf{a}$ of the vector $\mathbf{a}$ is defined by

$$\varDelta\mathbf{a} = a_{\alpha,\beta\gamma}\mathbf{e}^\alpha\, \mathbf{e}^\beta . \mathbf{e}^\gamma = g^{\beta\gamma}a_{\alpha,\beta\gamma}\, \mathbf{e}^\alpha.$$

The reader is asked to verify that this definition produces the same result as that of Section 66 in the case of a fundamental basis.

Hence we have

$$\text{grad div } \mathbf{a} - \varDelta\mathbf{a} = a_{\alpha,\beta\gamma}\, \mathbf{e}^\alpha . \mathbf{e}^\beta\, \mathbf{e}^\gamma - a_{\alpha,\beta\gamma}\, \mathbf{e}^\alpha\, \mathbf{e}^\beta . \mathbf{e}^\gamma$$

$$= a_{\alpha,\beta\gamma}\, \mathbf{e}^\beta \times (\mathbf{e}^\gamma \times \mathbf{e}^\alpha).$$

EXERCISES

1. Show that

$$\varDelta\mathbf{a} = g^{\beta\gamma}\left(\frac{\partial^2\mathbf{a}}{\partial u^\beta\, \partial u^\gamma} - \begin{Bmatrix}\sigma\\\beta\gamma\end{Bmatrix}\frac{\partial\mathbf{a}}{\partial u^\sigma}\right).$$

2. Using the result of Exercise 1 of Section 73, show that $a_{\alpha,\beta\gamma} = a_{\alpha,\gamma\beta}$.

76   Curl

Since $\text{curl } \mathbf{e}^\alpha = \mathbf{0}$, we have in virtue of (45.1) that

$$\text{curl } \mathbf{a} = \text{curl }(a_\alpha\mathbf{e}^\alpha)$$

$$= a_\alpha\, \text{curl } \mathbf{e}^\alpha + \text{grad } a_\alpha \times \mathbf{e}^\alpha$$

$$= \frac{\partial a_\alpha}{\partial u^\gamma}\, \mathbf{e}^\gamma \times \mathbf{e}^\alpha.$$

Since $\begin{Bmatrix}\sigma\\\alpha\gamma\end{Bmatrix}$ is symmetric in α and γ and $\mathbf{e}^\gamma \times \mathbf{e}^\alpha$ is skew-symmetric in α and γ, it follows that $\begin{Bmatrix}\sigma\\\alpha\gamma\end{Bmatrix}\mathbf{e}^\gamma \times \mathbf{e}^\alpha = \mathbf{0}$ and so

$$\text{curl } \mathbf{a} = a_{\alpha,\gamma}\, \mathbf{e}^\gamma \times \mathbf{e}^\alpha.$$

Further,

$$\text{curl curl } \mathbf{a} = \text{curl } (a_{\alpha,\gamma}\mathbf{e}^{\gamma} \times \mathbf{e}^{\alpha})$$

$$= \text{curl } (a_{\alpha,\gamma}\mathbf{e}^{\gamma} \times [\mathbf{e}^{\alpha}.\mathbf{e}_{\sigma}]\mathbf{e}^{\sigma})\dagger$$

$$= \left\{ \frac{\partial}{\partial u^{\rho}}(a_{\alpha,\gamma}\mathbf{e}^{\gamma} \times \mathbf{e}^{\alpha}.\mathbf{e}_{\sigma}) \right\}\mathbf{e}^{\rho} \times \mathbf{e}^{\sigma}$$

$$= \left\{ \frac{\partial a_{\alpha,\gamma}}{\partial u^{\rho}}[\mathbf{e}^{\gamma}\mathbf{e}^{\alpha}\mathbf{e}_{\sigma}] - a_{\alpha,\gamma}\left\{ \begin{matrix} \gamma \\ \rho\varepsilon \end{matrix} \right\}[\mathbf{e}^{\varepsilon}\mathbf{e}^{\alpha}\mathbf{e}_{\sigma}] - a_{\alpha,\gamma}\left\{ \begin{matrix} \alpha \\ \rho\varepsilon \end{matrix} \right\}[\mathbf{e}^{\gamma}\mathbf{e}^{\varepsilon}\mathbf{e}_{\sigma}] \right.$$

$$\left. + a_{\alpha,\gamma}\left\{ \begin{matrix} \varepsilon \\ \sigma\rho \end{matrix} \right\}[\mathbf{e}^{\gamma}\mathbf{e}^{\alpha}\mathbf{e}_{\varepsilon}] \right\}\mathbf{e}^{\rho} \times \mathbf{e}^{\sigma}.$$

The last summation vanishes since $\left\{ \begin{matrix} \varepsilon \\ \sigma\rho \end{matrix} \right\} \mathbf{e}^{\rho} \times \mathbf{e}^{\sigma} = \mathbf{0}$. Hence

$$\text{curl curl } \mathbf{a} = [\mathbf{e}^{\gamma}\mathbf{e}^{\alpha}\mathbf{e}_{\sigma}]\left\{ \frac{\partial a_{\alpha,\gamma}}{\partial u^{\rho}} - \left\{ \begin{matrix} \beta \\ \rho\gamma \end{matrix} \right\}a_{\alpha,\beta} - \left\{ \begin{matrix} \beta \\ \rho\alpha \end{matrix} \right\}a_{\beta,\gamma} \right\}\mathbf{e}^{\rho} \times \mathbf{e}^{\sigma}$$

$$= a_{\alpha,\gamma\rho}[\mathbf{e}^{\gamma}\mathbf{e}^{\alpha}\mathbf{e}_{\sigma}]\mathbf{e}^{\rho} \times \mathbf{e}^{\sigma}$$

$$= a_{\alpha,\gamma\rho}\mathbf{e}^{\rho} \times \{\mathbf{e}^{\gamma} \times [\mathbf{e}^{\alpha}.\mathbf{e}_{\sigma}]\mathbf{e}^{\sigma}\}$$

$$= a_{\alpha,\gamma\rho}\mathbf{e}^{\rho} \times (\mathbf{e}^{\gamma} \times \mathbf{e}^{\alpha}).\dagger$$

In virtue of Exercise 2 of the preceding section $a_{\alpha,\gamma\rho}$ is symmetrical in γ and ρ. Hence we have

$$\text{curl curl } \mathbf{a} = a_{\alpha,\rho\gamma}\mathbf{e}^{\rho} \times (\mathbf{e}^{\gamma} \times \mathbf{e}^{\alpha})$$

$$= a_{\alpha,\beta\gamma}\mathbf{e}^{\beta} \times (\mathbf{e}^{\gamma} \times \mathbf{e}^{\alpha}).$$

That is, we have established that

$$\text{curl curl } \mathbf{a} = \text{grad div } \mathbf{a} - \Delta\mathbf{a}.$$

It is well to emphasize that this relation holds for the tensor components referred to a natural basis, but not in general for the physical components of the vector $\mathbf{a}$.

$\dagger$ $(\mathbf{e}^{\alpha}.\mathbf{e}_{\sigma})\mathbf{e}^{\sigma} = \delta^{\alpha}_{\sigma}\mathbf{e}^{\sigma} = \mathbf{e}^{\alpha}.$

Solutions

Chapter 1

§ 1   1. (c) and (f) are vectors, others are scalars.

§ 6   1. (i) $\mathbf{b}-\mathbf{a}$, (ii) $-\mathbf{a}$, (iii) $-\mathbf{b}$, (iv) $\mathbf{a}-\mathbf{b}$, (v) $-2\mathbf{b}$, (vi) $2\mathbf{a}-2\mathbf{b}$.

      Components of $\overrightarrow{FA}$ are $-5\sqrt{3}/2$ and $5/2$.

      Components of $\overrightarrow{FE}$ are $5\sqrt{3}/2$ and $5/2$.

    2. $\overrightarrow{AB}=\alpha+\beta+\gamma$, $\overrightarrow{CA}=-\alpha-\beta$, projected vector is $-(\alpha+\beta)/2$.

§ 7   1. (i) $6\mathbf{i}-3\mathbf{j}+2\mathbf{k}$, (ii) $3\sqrt{5}$, (iii) $-(6\mathbf{i}+6\mathbf{j}-5\mathbf{k})/\sqrt{(97)}$.

§ 8   2. (ii) $\sin^{-1}(31/50)$, (iii) $\pm(\mathbf{i}-11\mathbf{j}-7\mathbf{k})/\sqrt{(171)}$.

§ 9   2. (i) $-3(\mathbf{i}+\mathbf{j}+\mathbf{k})$, $-(2\mathbf{i}+\mathbf{j}+2\mathbf{k})$, $-(\mathbf{i}+2\mathbf{j}+4\mathbf{k})$, (ii) $\pm(2\mathbf{i}+\mathbf{j}+2\mathbf{k})/3$,
      (iii) $\sqrt{(21)}/2$.

§ 10 1. 1.

§ 11 3. (i) -22, (ii) $27\mathbf{i}+4\mathbf{j}-11\mathbf{k}$, (iii) $-2(5\mathbf{i}+\mathbf{j}-9\mathbf{k})$, (iv) $11(2\mathbf{i}+4\mathbf{j}-6\mathbf{k})$
      (v) 540, (vi) $-11(54\mathbf{i}+8\mathbf{j}-11\mathbf{k})$.

§ 13 1. $\frac{1}{2}(\mathbf{j}+\mathbf{k})$, $\frac{1}{2}(\mathbf{k}+\mathbf{i})$, $\frac{1}{2}(\mathbf{i}+\mathbf{j})$.

MISCELLANEOUS EXERCISES

    1. $(\mathbf{b}\times\mathbf{c})/[\mathbf{abc}]$.

Chapter 2

MISCELLANEOUS EXERCISES

    1. 7.

    2. $9/\sqrt{(17)}$.

    3. $58/(5\sqrt{2})$.

    9. (a) $\cos^{-1}\frac{1}{3}$, (b) $\cos^{-1}1/\sqrt{3}$.

Chapter 3

§ 19 2. $\mathbf{p}=\frac{1}{6}u^3\mathbf{a}+\frac{1}{2}u^2\mathbf{b}$.

§ 23 2. (i) $(1+u^2)\sin u-u\cos u$,
      (ii) $(u^3\sin u-3u^2\cos u)\mathbf{i}+(u^3\cos u+3u^2\sin u)\mathbf{j}$
      $+(\cos u+u\sin u+u^2\cos u)\mathbf{k}$.

§ 24 1. (i) $ve^{uv}\mathbf{i}+2\mathbf{j}+v\cos u\,\mathbf{k}$, (ii) $v^2e^{uv}\mathbf{i}-v\sin u\,\mathbf{k}$,
      (iii) $(1+uv)e^{uv}\mathbf{i}+\cos u\,\mathbf{k}$, (iv) $u^2e^{uv}\mathbf{i}$,
      (v) $(2\sin u+v\cos u)\mathbf{i}+v(u\cos u-\sin u)e^{uv}\mathbf{j}-(2u+v)e^{uv}\mathbf{k}$.

    2. (i) 0, (ii) $-36\mathbf{j}$.

Chapter 4

§ 28 1. $(-\dot{f} \cos v \,\mathbf{i} - \dot{f} \sin v \,\mathbf{j} + \mathbf{k})/\sqrt{(1+\dot{f}^2)}$.

2. $\left(\dfrac{df}{dv} \sin v \,\mathbf{i} - \dfrac{df}{dv} \cos v \,\mathbf{j} + u\mathbf{k}\right) \Big/ \sqrt{\left\{u^2 + \left(\dfrac{df}{dv}\right)^2\right\}}$.

§ 29 1. $a^2(du^2 + \sin^2 u \, dv^2)$, $(1+\dot{f}^2)\,du^2 + u^2\,dv^2$, $du^2 + \left\{u^2 + \left(\dfrac{df}{dv}\right)^2\right\} dv^2$.

3. $-a(du^2 + \sin^2 v \, dv^2)$, $(\ddot{f}\,du^2 + u\dot{f}\,dv^2)/(1+\dot{f}^2)^{1/2}$,

$\left(2\dfrac{df}{dv}\,du\,dv - v^2\dfrac{d^2f}{dv^2} ^2\right) \Big/ \left(u^2 + \left(\dfrac{df}{dv}\right)^2\right)^{1/2}$.

Chapter 5

§ 32 1. (i) 0, (ii) 0.

2. (i) 2, (ii) 3, (iii) $2\frac{17}{140}$.

§ 33 1. $\rho(e^{2\pi} - 1)\mathbf{k}$.

§ 35 1. $6(\mathbf{i}+\mathbf{j}+\mathbf{k})$, 0, $\mathbf{0}$.

2. $1/8$.

§ 36 1. $24\mathbf{i} + 96\mathbf{j} + 394\mathbf{k}/5$.

Chapter 6

§ 37 1. (i) $7\sqrt{6}/2$, (ii) $-9/\sqrt{2}$, (iii) $1/\sqrt{2}$.　　2. $2\mathbf{A}.\boldsymbol{\alpha}$.

§ 38 1. (i) 2, (ii) $\sqrt{3}$, (iii) $\sqrt{(14)}$.

§ 39 3. No, (ii) Yes, $\frac{1}{2}(\boldsymbol{\lambda}.\boldsymbol{\mu})r^2$, (iii) Yes, $(\boldsymbol{\lambda}.\mathbf{r})(\boldsymbol{\mu}.\mathbf{r})$, (iv) No.

Chapter 7

§ 41 3. (i) $2(x+y+z)$, (ii) 0, (iii) zx, (iv) 0,

(v) $yz(2x+y+z)\mathbf{i} + zx(x+2y+z)\mathbf{j} + xy(x+y+2z)\mathbf{k}$,

(vi) 0, (vii) $2zx(z-x)(x^2 + 6y^2 + z^2 + zx)$.

4. (i) 0, (ii) 6, (iii) $\dfrac{d^2f}{dr^2} + \dfrac{2}{r}\dfrac{df}{dr}$, (iv) $\dfrac{2}{r^4}$.

§ 42 1. 0.

3. $4\pi(a+b+c)/3$.

§ 43 1. c/r^3 for any constant c.

Chapter 8

§ 44 1. (i) $\mathbf{i}+\mathbf{j}-\mathbf{k}$, (ii) $-\mathbf{i}+\mathbf{j}-\mathbf{k}$, (iii) $\mathbf{0}$, (iv) 0,

(v) $(3y^2z + 3yz^2 + 2xy^2 + 2xz^2)\mathbf{i} + z(3x^2 + 3zx - 2yz)\mathbf{j}$
$+ y(3x^2 + 3xy - 2yz)\mathbf{k}$, (vi) 0, (vii) $\mathbf{0}$.

§ 45 2. (i) $e^{x+y+z}\{x(y-z)\mathbf{i} + y(z-x)\mathbf{j} + z(x-y)\mathbf{k}\}$,

(ii) $x(ze^z - ye^y)\mathbf{i} + y(xe^x - ze^z)\mathbf{j} + z(ye^y - xe^x)\mathbf{k}$.

Chapter 9

§ 50 1. See equation (44.3).

§ 55 2. (i) $(y^2+z^2)\mathbf{i} + (z^2+x^2)\mathbf{j} + (x^2+y^2)\mathbf{k}$, (ii) $r^3\mathbf{r} \times (\mathbf{r} \times \mathbf{c})/6$,

(iii) $\frac{1}{4}\{x(z^2-y^2)\mathbf{i} + y(x^2-z^2)\mathbf{j} + z(y^2-x^2)\mathbf{k}\}$,

(iv) $(xe^x + 1 - e^x)(z\mathbf{i} - x\mathbf{k})/x^2$.

Chapter 11

§ 62 1. (i) $h_1 = h_2 = \sqrt{(u^2+v^2)}$, $h_3 = 1$,

$\mathbf{I} = (u\mathbf{i}+v\mathbf{j})/\sqrt{(u^2+v^2)}$, $\mathbf{J} = (-v\mathbf{i}+u\mathbf{j})/\sqrt{(u^2+v^2)}$, $\mathbf{K} = \mathbf{k}$,

(ii) $h_1 = h_2 = \sqrt{(u^2+v^2)}$, $h_3 = uv$;

$\mathbf{I} = (v\cos w\,\mathbf{i} + v\sin w\,\mathbf{j} + u\mathbf{k})/\sqrt{(u^2+v^2)}$,

$\mathbf{J} = (u\cos w\,\mathbf{i} + u\sin w\,\mathbf{j} - v\mathbf{k})/\sqrt{(u^2+v^2)}$,

$\mathbf{K} = -\sin w\,\mathbf{i} + \cos w\,\mathbf{j}$.

(iii) $h_1 = a\sqrt{\{(u^2-v^2)/(u^2-1)\}}$, $h_2 = a\sqrt{\{(u^2-v^2)/(1-v^2)\}}$,

$h_3 = a\sqrt{\{(u^2-1)(1-v^2)\}}$;

$$\mathbf{I} = u\sqrt{\left(\frac{1-v^2}{u^2-v^2}\right)}\{\cos w\,\mathbf{i} + \sin w\,\mathbf{j}\} + v\sqrt{\left(\frac{u^2-1}{u^2-v^2}\right)}\mathbf{k},$$

$$\mathbf{J} = -v\sqrt{\left(\frac{u^2-1}{u^2-v^2}\right)}\{\cos w\,\mathbf{i} + \sin w\,\mathbf{j}\} + u\sqrt{\left(\frac{1-v^2}{u^2-v^2}\right)}\mathbf{k},$$

$\mathbf{K} = -\sin w\,\mathbf{i} + \cos w\,\mathbf{j}$.

§ 63 1. $\left(\dfrac{\partial f}{\partial u}\mathbf{I} + \dfrac{\partial f}{\partial v}\mathbf{J}\right)\big/\sqrt{(u^2+v^2)} + \dfrac{\partial f}{\partial w}\mathbf{K}$,

(ii) $\left(\dfrac{\partial f}{\partial u}\mathbf{I} + \dfrac{\partial f}{\partial v}\mathbf{J}\right)\big/\sqrt{(u^2+v^2)} + \dfrac{\partial f}{\partial w}\mathbf{K}/(uv)$,

(iii) $\left\{\sqrt{(u^2-1)}\,\dfrac{\partial f}{\partial u}\mathbf{I} + \sqrt{(1-v^2)}\,\dfrac{\partial f}{\partial v}\mathbf{J}\right\}\big/\{a\sqrt{(u^2-v^2)}\}$

$+ \dfrac{\partial f}{\partial w}\mathbf{K}[a\sqrt{\{(u^2-1)(1-v^2)\}}]$.

§ 64 2. (i) $\dfrac{1}{u^2+v^2}\left\{\dfrac{\partial}{\partial u}\left(\sqrt{(u^2+v^2)}a_I\right) + \dfrac{\partial}{\partial v}\left(\sqrt{(u^2+v^2)}a_J\right) + (u^2+v^2)\dfrac{\partial a_K}{\partial w}\right\}$;

$\dfrac{1}{u^2+v^2}\left\{\dfrac{\partial^2 f}{\partial u^2} + \dfrac{\partial^2 f}{\partial v^2}\right\} + \dfrac{\partial^2 f}{\partial w^2}$,

(ii) $\dfrac{1}{uv(u^2+v^2)}\left\{\dfrac{\partial}{\partial u}\left[uv\sqrt{(u^2+v^2)}a_I\right] + \dfrac{\partial}{\partial v}\left[uv\sqrt{(u^2+v^2)}a_J\right]\right\}$

$+ \dfrac{1}{uv}\dfrac{\partial a_K}{\partial w}$,

$\dfrac{1}{uv(u^2+v^2)}\left\{\dfrac{\partial}{\partial u}\left(uv\dfrac{\partial f}{\partial u}\right) + \dfrac{\partial}{\partial v}\left(uv\dfrac{\partial f}{\partial v}\right)\right\} + \dfrac{1}{u^2v^2}\dfrac{\partial^2 f}{\partial w^2}$,

(iii) $\dfrac{1}{a(u^2-v^2)}\left\{\dfrac{\partial}{\partial u}\left(\sqrt{\{(u^2-1)(u^2-v^2)\}}a_I\right)\right.$

$\left. + \dfrac{\partial}{\partial v}\left(\sqrt{\{(1-v^2)(u^2-v^2)\}}\,a_J\right)\right\}$

$+ \dfrac{1}{a\sqrt{\{(u^2-1)(1-v^2)\}}}\dfrac{\partial a_K}{\partial w}$;

$\dfrac{1}{a^2(u^2-v^2)}\left\{\dfrac{\partial}{\partial u}\left[(u^2-1)\dfrac{\partial f}{\partial u}\right] + \dfrac{\partial}{\partial v}\left[(1-v^2)\dfrac{\partial f}{\partial v}\right]\right\}$

$+ \dfrac{1}{a^2(u^2-1)(1-v^2)}\dfrac{\partial^2 f}{\partial w^2}$.

§ 65   1. (i) $\dfrac{1}{\sqrt{(u^2+v^2)}}\left\{\dfrac{\partial a_K}{\partial v}\,\mathbf{I}-\dfrac{\partial a_K}{\partial u}\,\mathbf{J}\right\}+\dfrac{\partial a_I}{\partial w}\,\mathbf{J}-\dfrac{\partial a_J}{\partial w}\,\mathbf{I}$

$\qquad\qquad+\dfrac{1}{u^2+v^2}\left\{\dfrac{\partial}{\partial u}\left(\sqrt{(u^2+v^2)}a_J\right)-\dfrac{\partial}{\partial v}\left(\sqrt{(u^2+v^2)}a_I\right)\right\}\mathbf{K},$

(ii) $\dfrac{1}{uv\sqrt{(u^2+v^2)}}\left\{u\,\dfrac{\partial}{\partial v}\,(v\,a_K)\mathbf{I}-v\,\dfrac{\partial}{\partial u}\,(u\,a_K)\mathbf{J}\right\}$

$\qquad\quad+\dfrac{1}{uv}\left\{\dfrac{\partial a_I}{\partial w}\,\mathbf{J}-\dfrac{\partial a_J}{\partial w}\,\mathbf{I}\right\}$

$\qquad\quad+\dfrac{1}{u^2+v^2}\left\{\dfrac{\partial}{\partial u}\left(\sqrt{(u^2+v^2)}a_J\right)-\dfrac{\partial}{\partial v}\left(\sqrt{(u^2+v^2)}a_I\right)\right\}\,\mathbf{K},$

(iii) $\dfrac{1}{a\sqrt{\{(u^2-1)(u^2-v^2)\}}}\left\{\dfrac{\partial}{\partial v}\left(\sqrt{\{(u^2-1)(1-v^2)\}}a_K\right)-\sqrt{\left(\dfrac{u^2-v^2}{1-v^2}\right)}\dfrac{\partial a_J}{\partial w}\right\}\mathbf{I}$

$\qquad+\dfrac{1}{a\sqrt{\{(1-v^2)(u^2-v^2)\}}}\left\{\sqrt{\left(\dfrac{u^2-v^2}{u^2-1}\right)}\dfrac{\partial a_I}{\partial w}-\dfrac{\partial}{\partial u}\left(\sqrt{\{u^2-1)(1-v^2)\}}a_K\right)\right\}\mathbf{J}$

$\qquad+\dfrac{\sqrt{\{(1-v^2)(u^2-1)\}}}{a(u^2-v^2)}\left\{\dfrac{\partial}{\partial u}\left(\sqrt{\left(\dfrac{u^2-v^2}{1-v^2}\right)}a_J\right)-\dfrac{\partial}{\partial v}\left(\sqrt{\left(\dfrac{u^2-v^2}{u^2-1}\right)}a_I\right)\right\}\mathbf{K}.$

Index